GAME CHANGER

World War 2, Radar, the Atomic Bomb, and
the Life of Kenneth Tompkins Bainbridge

DAVID A. BAINBRIDGE

Contents

"Bainbridge was one of these wonderful people that you wish you could meet all the time because he was very generous and very interested in helping people."

— Alfred O. C. Nier
  Nominee Nobel Prize in Physics 1949
  NASA Medal for Exceptional Scientific Achievement 1977

Prolog

P hysicist Kenneth Tompkins Bainbridge played a crucial role in World War II and his efforts were of great value in winning the war. It has been called "the physicist's war" and said that the atomic bomb may have ended the war, but radar won it. Ken's contributions to both efforts were foreshadowed by his previous pioneering research in physics—including his fellowships at the Bartol Foundation and then the Cavendish Laboratory in Cambridge, England. His many research projects, engineering innovation, and patents developed from his student work at General Electric Company all helped him facilitate the industrial production of needed radar components.

Ken was the first scientist recruited by E. O. Lawrence for the new Radiation Lab (radar research) at MIT in 1940. He was tasked with finding the space and setting it up, even before the U.S. entered the war. He recruited people for both scientific work and staff support, served on the administration committee for the lab, and added his own engineering and physics skills to radar development. He chose to take on the modulator group—a key component and one that saw rapid and impressive improvements. One of the members of the research team later said Ken was a central figure in the development of improved radar for ships and planes that could detect the German submarines that were decimating Allied shipping. The advanced cavity magnetron-based radar systems developed at the lab could not be detected by the U-boats. This meant U-boats now had to consider running submerged with a snorkel raised to supply oxygen to the diesel engines, limiting the top speed to 6 knots instead of 18 knots on the surface. This hampered their ability to organize "wolf packs," hampered their hunting, and reduced ship losses.

Ken's third role, for which he is best known, was as the director of the first atomic bomb test in New Mexico (1943-1945). He was recruited by J. Robert Oppenheimer and General Leslie Groves to work on the design of high explosive assemblies for the atomic bomb. In recognition of his skill and ability, he was soon appointed overall director of the Trinity test in March 1945. For this, he had to select the site, develop the research program, select the staff, oversee the installation of the bomb, and then carry out the explosion. His experience and education provided excellent training for this challenging project, dealing with scientists, engineers, fabricators, vendors, and the army. The success of the test on July 16 led to the use of the atomic bombs on Nagasaki and Hiroshima and the end of the war. The allied military forces had been planning a two-pronged invasion of the Japanese mainland with an estimated one million casualties and the death of ten million Japanese civilians and military.

Realizing the enormity of the unleashing of the atomic bomb, Ken remarked, "Now we are all sons of bitches." He went on to work for civilian control of the nuclear effort, helped establish the Federation of American Scientists, and worked for bans on testing and a promise to never use the H-bomb first.

Ken made the extra effort to carefully document his work and to check and recheck calculations. He was concerned about the well being of his staff and colleagues and accepted people as they were. This enabled him to work well with people from many different backgrounds and responsibilities. At the Trinity base camp, he made changes to improve the quality of life for the scientists and for the soldiers involved in support and security.

Ken is little known today because he was modest and focused on his work. He was quick to credit others for their contributions and support, and less concerned about his reputation than some of the other scientists and engineers. (He was also more serious about the need for tight security than some of the scientists.)

Ken was a good father and husband, making time for his children when he could, even during the war. They said when he was home, he was there for them, willing to play games or just to talk. Even as he reached his eighties, the neighborhood children were still stopping at the cottage on Martha's Vineyard and asking, "Would Mr. Bainbridge like to play?"

We will do well to remember and appreciate the life of this ethical man who also happened to be a brilliant engineer and scientist.

Childhood

1904-1921

823 Riverside Drive

CHAPTER 1

Childhood

K enneth Tompkins Bainbridge entered the world on July 27, 1904, in Cooperstown, New York. His father William Warin Bainbridge and mother Mae Louise (Tompkins) Bainbridge lived in New York City but were in Cooperstown to beat the heat, with NYC reaching a steamy 94°F on July 19th. Cooperstown was easily reached by rail, first to Oneonta and then traveling by electric train to the village. It was a favorite, fashionable spot for the summer refugees of the Gilded Age.

Ken's father William was a stationer (paper sales, printing, office supplies, etc.), as was his grandfather John George Bainbridge, great-grandfather Henry, and many of the Bainbridge cousins. Ken never said much about his father; he may not have been an engaged parent. The family had a maid and Ken may have had a more 19th century style upbringing.

Ken's mother Mae (Mary Louise Tompkins) was a Catholic New Yorker, distantly related to Daniel D. Tompkins, the governor of New York from 1807–1817, and then vice president of the US under James Monroe from 1817–1825. Her family seems to have been relatively well-off. Ken's maternal grandmother Kate Tompkins (Katherine née O'Neill) lived with the family for several years at Riverside Drive. Ken's mother outlived two of her sons and made it to the age of 91, instilling a great deal of confidence in her children and grandchildren. She worked with the

Red Cross for years, greeting troop ships during World War I and fudging her age to do it again in World War II.

FIGURE 1-2:   Bill, Don, Ken

FIGURE 1-3: William Warin Bainbridge

Ken was the middle of three brothers, with William, Jr. the oldest by two years, and Donald younger by five. Ken was an altar boy but he quit the church at age thirteen after a priest told him not to hang out with the Jewish or Protestant boys at Horace Mann school. Bill was more athletic and went on to represent MIT in intercollegiate sports, and Ken was on the hockey team at Horace Mann. The three boys must have been quite a handful, surely making for a lively household.

Ken's childhood home, a three-story brownstone, was at 823 Riverside Drive (at 158th) in Washington Heights, Manhattan. By the early nineteenth century, Washington Heights was dotted with large country homes of wealthy New Yorkers, but the area remained rural with many wooded areas; even grazing cows could be found.

FIGURE 1-4:   Mae Tompkins Bainbridge

The home Ken grew up in had a splendid view of the river and was brand new, completed in 1900, the year his parents were married. The lot sloped steeply so even the basement kitchen and maid's room had windows providing plenty of light on the river side. Steep stairs led up to the first floor with a sunlit dining room. A dumbwaiter was used to bring food up to the dining room, breakfast to Grandmother Kate, and milk and treats to the children's rooms.

In 1905, William bought a two-and-a-half acre lot in Briar-cliff Manor, about 30 miles upriver. He intended to build a new house there, joining the Vanderbilts, Astors and other wealthy families, but the family fortune may have been hard hit by the Panic of 1907 as the market dropped 50%. In 1910, William was advertising the Briarcliff Manor lot for sale and the house at Riverside Drive for summer lease. Fortunately, the Riverside Drive house remained in the family into the 1950s. It was valued at $40,000 in the 1930 census.

The area was named for Fort Washington, constructed at the highest point on Manhattan Island by Continental Army troops during the Revolutionary War. Washington Heights is bordered by Harlem to the south, along 155th Street, Inwood to the north along Hillside Avenue, the Hudson River to the west, and the Harlem River and Coogan's Bluff to the east.

It was an ideal location for an active boy. The house was close to the Hudson and Harlem rivers, parks and piers, and it was the heyday of bicycling. The streets were smooth but still had relatively few cars. Their father may not have been a baseball fan, but the boys apparently were. If they could scrape together fifty cents or a dollar, they could buy a ticket. Alternatively, they could watch for free from Coogan's Bluff. They only had to walk seven blocks north to get to the baseball field at Hilltop Park, and four blocks east to the Polo Grounds. Hilltop Park was the home of the Yankees (also called the Highlanders at the time) from 1903–1912, and many games included Babe Ruth. From 1913 on, the Yankees shared the Polo Grounds with their arch rival, the Giants. In 1921, the Yankees won the American League Series but lost the World Series to the Giants. The Olympic athletes that were headed to Stockholm in 1912 made a stop at Hilltop Park for publicity photos. It is likely Ken went to see them, perhaps with his uncle George, the United States national foils fencing champion of 1908. There was also a large amusement park within easy distance on foot, bike, or streetcar, at Fort George. Like many kids, the boys may have managed to make it onto the rollercoaster, despite parental warning not to do so.

FIGURE 1-5:   Playtime

The seasons brought many changes to Washington Heights, certainly affecting the Bainbridge home and activities. Some years the kids had big snow to play with, including sledding down the hills, streets, and parks. On December 30, 1917, the temperature dropped to -13°F; more than fifty inches of snow fell that year—a boon to kids but a challenge for everyone else. The summers could be hot and humid. On one steamy day in August 1918, the thermometer shot up to 104°F, prompting the hydrants to be opened so kids could cool off in the streets. The luckier residents escaped the heat by heading north to places like the Catskills, the Adirondacks, Cooperstown, or Maine.

Rural workers were moving to the city for employment, and the tenements filled with immigrants as the population of the city rose from 343,000 in 1900, to 562,000 in 1920. Washington Heights, now the home of Yeshiva University, would become an immigrant area later, populated by many Irish and Jewish families. Today it is multicultural, with growing numbers of professionals and those working in the medical field.

Ken attended Horace Mann School (1910–1915) and the Horace Mann High School (1915–1921). This private school was founded in 1887 as a coeducational experimental school by the Teacher's College of Columbia University. The goal was to test progressive educational theories under the observation of Teacher's College students. In 1901, the Horace Mann School moved into its own building at 120th Street and Broadway in Morningside Heights. There were 600 lower division and 300 upper division students. The school was across the street from the former Bloomingdale Insane Asylum, then being used as a student dormitory by Teacher's College. As former resident housing advisors would note, this was fitting.

By the time Ken arrived, Horace Mann was less experimental and more well-regarded as a prep school for the Ivy League universities.[1] Ken started at the elementary school near Columbia

University. In 1914, the boy's division of the school moved to the Riverdale section of the Bronx, where it pioneered the country day school movement. The large fields this area provided were good for sports and exercise. Horace Mann also operated a summer camp, Camp Moosilauke in New Hampshire, that Ken and the other boys attended.

The Horace Mann Schools

Teachers College, Columbia University
Superior Equipment for all Grades
of School Work

A BROAD, GENERAL PREPARATION FOR COLLEGE AND FOR LIFE

" For the first time a child may enter the Kindergarten and go forward, in unbroken course, until he passes out into the world with the highest honors of a modern university. " —*President Butler, of Columbia University*.

NEW PUPILS RECEIVED AS VACANCIES OCCUR.

Illustrated Circular sent on application.

VIRGIL PRETTYMAN, Prin.   SAMUEL T. DUTTON, Supt.

The patience to be thorough, the concentration to understand, and the persistence to grasp and apply. Original motto.

Magna est Veritas et Praevalet
Great is the Truth and it Prevails   Revised motto, 1952

FIGURE 1-6:   Horace Mann School

Camp Moosilauke

FIGURE 1-7:   Moosilauke, the Horace Mann Summer Camp

In 1918, the Spanish flu hit New York hard, leaving more than 20,000 dead from flu or pneumonia. Just four years earlier, in

1914, Horace Mann worked to minimize the risk of TB among the student body by initiating rooftop and outdoor classrooms. These proved invaluable during the flu epidemic. The fresh air classrooms were described as "closed on three sides only, the south side being entirely open with a drop curtain to close that side in time of storm." Children could nip into warm rooms, if necessary, but these were most likely reserved for exceptional cases. Students handled the cold by wrapping themselves in "sitting out bags."

Horace Mann was a powerhouse Ivy League prep school (as it is today) with advanced classes and skilled teachers. Ken received a solid preparation in mathematics, physics, chemistry, and biology. The school also encouraged active team sports, exercise, community building, governance, and preparation for a meaningful life in business and community. Ken was on the ice hockey team in 1921, managed the baseball team, and was a member of the Lynx Club. These school social clubs were much like fraternities. His brother Bill lettered in football and also played hockey. No doubt they kept the street in front of the house ringing with practice shots and enjoyed the nearby skating rinks in winter.

Ken was involved in the school publications, including *the Mannikin* and *Horace Mann Record*. Students were expected to assist with administration of the school and were responsible for preparing large social events both in and out of school. Ken was a member of the Student Council, and Quarterly Committee in 1920. The Lynx Club organized a successful excursion by train to have dinner with the Scarsdale Young Woman's Wayside Club (a hot bed of suffragettes about 25 miles away). In 1921, the Lynx Club held a tea at the library for 170 alumni. In his senior year, Ken was on both the commencement committee and General Administration executive committee.

Outdoor cooking

Study sack for fresh
air classrooms

FIGURE 1-8:   Outdoor cooking, study sack at Horace Mann

FIGURE 1-9:   Fresh air classroom Grace Dodge
Hall, and rooftop exercise at Horace Mann

FIGURE 1-10: Horace Mann Plebe Class and Lynx Club

Ken's teachers at Horace Mann certainly had a hand in shaping his thinking, but his two uncles also influenced him, as both were engineers. Uncle George was an inventor, credited with more than 100 patents and inventions. He was also a machinist, and he designed and manufactured equipment for a wide range of tasks. Ken's Uncle Jack (John G., Jr.) had an engineering degree from Stevens Institute of Technology and served in army aviation in WWI. He worked in the Bainbridge paper companies and was named president of Bainbridge, Kimpton, and Haupt in 1924. He stayed at the Riverside house with his sister-in-law for almost 30 years.

Ken was in the radio club at Horace Mann and built a radio room on the third floor of the house, putting an antenna on the roof. The antenna and ground were connected across vibrating contacts, energizing an ultraviolet unit to send out a radio pulse. He was able to communicate with Morse code. He realized later that he must have violated every bandwidth law— but these were pioneering times.

Ken could see the Hudson River, full of ships, including ferries, freighters, and military vessels. Navy ships sometimes docked at the 159th Street pier. Many of the navy ships were equipped with new wireless telephones made by Western Electric and the navy operators were having a picnic with their new toys. They talked to each other, told jokes, and conversed with the amateurs, who were very interested in their equipment. As Ken's friend Giles Rich noted, "You only had to go down to a dock to get a free ride in a navy launch to any ship you wanted to visit." Radio pioneer Lee de Forest wanted to acquire some of the vacuum tubes the navy used. He could not get them from the phone company, so he made deals with amateurs who would buy them from the navy operators and then sell them to him. One day, Ken invited Giles along to buy a couple of spare tubes that they took over to the De Forest Radio Telephone & Telegraph Company, where they watched de Forest test them; that is how Ken and Giles got to meet the famous inventor. A strictly illegal transaction, but the statute of limitations has long run its course.

Ship radio operators would sometimes knock on the door of Ken's house to visit or ask who had erected the antenna and was on the air. This worked out well, as radiomen would sell Ken rare 5-watt vacuum tubes for a couple of dollars before they "headed to town." With these, he built a radiotelephone and obtained his amateur radio license. He operated a 5-watt ham station with the call letters 2WN (this was before the national prefix "W" was added to call letters). His interaction with other radio operators stimulated his interest in electrical engineering, science, and technology, but he did not continue his radio work once he left home. It is worth noting that he did remain interested and involved, keeping a marine band radio later in life at Martha's Vineyard to monitor ship traffic in the summer.

On April 13, 1921, tragedy struck when William, having suffered from ill health for some time and severe head pain the day before, committed suicide by inhaling illuminating gas. He was 45 years old, and Ken was only 16. It is possible he was suffering from the long-term impacts of the Spanish Flu.[2] Many people who survived the flu had long term disability. Mental problems and fatigue were particularly common, often lasting for years. There is some suggestion his brother Arthur was not sympathetic. As today, with Covid-19 long haulers, the failure to work hard was, and is, often seen as mental or moral weakness.

William's health problems had already led to his retirement from the stationers' firm of Henry Bainbridge & Company in January 1920. The family finances diminished; but money was always found for schools and education. Several land transfers in later years suggest William may have invested in land in other areas aside from Briarcliff Manor, and this may have kept the family afloat. After 1921, the family walked everywhere, rarely spending the 5¢ for the street cars. Years later, when the grandchildren visited, they also walked with their grandmother, going as far upriver as the George Washington Bridge and to museums and other attractions. Mae was an anglophile and did splurge to take the grandchildren to high tea at the English-Speaking Union at 345 Madison Avenue.

Riverside Drive

The Fleet on the Hudson

FIGURE 1-11:   Riverside Drive and Battleship Row

In the summer of 1921, Ken visited his uncle George in California. He said this was a restorative time and relief from the sadness at home. With the help of his machinist/inventor uncle, Ken built a small, working steam locomotive.

When asked why he choose to study science, Ken said it may have started when he got a Chemcraft chemistry set as a child. He enjoyed it and said he was making things right and left. He also enjoyed playing with the Lionel toy train sets passed down by his uncle George. These beautifully produced trains probably encouraged his thinking about engineering and design.

He headed to MIT in the fall.

FIGURE 1-12:   Horace Mann Senior 1921

MIT

1921-1926

·THE EAST TOWER·

Mens et Manus   Hands and Mind

CHAPTER 2

MIT

After his father's death, Ken was probably relieved to follow his brother off to the Massachusetts Institute of Technology (MIT) in Cambridge, Massachusetts. He found a challenging program of courses and research, interesting students, and a capable faculty. When he arrived in 1921, MIT had more than 3,500 students, with 635 in electrical engineering, the largest department, and 14 in aeronautical engineering. International students made up 7.5% of the enrollment—high for the time. Chinese students were most numerous, followed by Canadians, Brits, Mexicans, and Russians. Women were allowed but were a very small minority. The tuition was $300 per year, a considerable sum at the time. Many students also had to pay laboratory fees.

The 1922 catalog clearly lays out the philosophy and intent of MIT. The goal, as stated, was "to provide students with a combination of general, scientific and professional training that will fit them to take leading positions as engineers, scientific experts, and teachers and investigators of science." The school included twelve professional departments as well as Engineering Administration. Ken took Electrical Engineering and Aeronautical Engineering. Students could also choose from English and History, Economics, Statistics, Mathematics, Military Science, Modern Languages, and Physical Training. MIT maintained several research labs, including Electrical Engineering and Aerodynamics. Monthly meetings, open to all students, reported on and discussed research work.

FIGURE 2-2:   Engineering Lab MIT

The emphasis of the university, then and now, was to provide preparation for professional practice. Entering students had to be well prepared to pass entrance exams in math, foreign languages, physics, trigonometry, and algebra. Exams could be taken in lieu of some classes. Certificates were allowed as credit for other subjects, including geometry, history, chemistry, biology, and English.

Ken chose an electrical engineering program that included a cooperative program with industry.[3] For his corporate work, he chose the engineering department at General Electric. He started at GE's Lynn, Massachusetts plant in his sophomore year, but also spent time at their much larger operation in Schenectady, New York. Room and board (like at a B&B) in a family home in Schenectady cost $6–8 a week.

FIGURE 2-3:   GE Factory Complex, Schenectady

FIGURE 2-4:   Drafting Class at GE

The co-op program involved a great deal of work with few breaks, but it provided excellent training and a BS and MS degree in five years. In his final graduate year, Ken took physics classes with Manuel Vallarta and Hans Mueller. Mueller was noted for his efforts to improve undergraduate physics and his studies of the dielectric and optical properties of crystals and the photo-elastic effect. Ken also studied aeronautical engineering. After completing this corporate/collegiate education it was expected one would step directly into GE's engineering department.

The industrial training would prove invaluable in Ken's subsequent research and project management. He learned how to use machine tools including shapers, lathes, boring machines, drill presses, and grinders. He also studied drafting and worked in the General Electric Company's engineering department, developing relay devices.

FIGURE 2-5:   Boring machine trainee at GE

Ken tested streetlight transformers and calibrated meters. He also became familiar with large machines and oscillographs while testing equipment to the failure point in GE's Switch Gear Testing Department.

> ### Electrical Engineering, Course VI. Overview (Ken's program of study)
>
> Electrical Engineering included the study of mathematics, chemistry, physics, and applied mechanics in the earlier years, and the theory of electricity and magnetism began in the second year and continued through the remainder of the course. In addition, students studied steam hydraulic power engineering, the design of structures and machines, and political economy. In the junior and senior years, specialized courses covered the applications of electricity to a range of problems in railroads, power stations, power transmission, lighting, telephony, etc. Lab work began with chemistry and physics and extended through all scientific branches. The laboratories were extensively equipped with apparatus to meet the needs of undergraduate and advanced study. The laboratory work was designed to develop a habit of accurate observation, application of fundamental science, methods, and tests. Students would also learn to address questions of time and efficiency. The program culminated with a thesis requiring originality and application of acquired technique.

Work at General Electric

The co-op course with GE provided Ken with training on the technical and executive responsibilities of the electrical manufacturing industries and public utilities. His last three years were divided equally between instruction at MIT and practical training at GE. In his final year, he learned more about the administration of large manufacturing enterprises, the design and development of engineering projects, and creative research.

Ken was a member of the MIT Post Society of American Military Engineers. All of this training and experience proved to be invaluable twenty years later during the war.

His work at MIT and GE was exemplary and productive, leading to developments and patents in photo-cathode materials for photocells and the amplification of photocurrents by secondary emission cathodes. This work would eventually advance the development of movies and television. His improvement of electromagnetic pumps for liquids, used for refrigeration purposes in household refrigerators, would later find application in the circulating pumps of nuclear reactors. Ironically, when he visited later in life, they would not let him see what he had been working on — it was classified.

MIT outside the classroom

Although the co-op program kept him busy, it was not all academics. Ken was in the honor society Tau Beta Pi TBΠ[4] and Alpha Tau Omega ATΩ (along with his brother William). By the time Ken graduated, he had been class secretary, class treasurer, served on the finance committee, and worked on the MIT VooDoo humor magazine. He also met Alexander Macomber, an electrical engineer and utility executive, MIT Class of 1907. Macomber was active in the ATΩ fraternity, an MIT Corporation Member, and President of the MIT Alumni Association. Macomber took an interest in Ken and became a mentor, and perhaps, a substitute father figure. Ken later traveled with him to Europe to visit mines and, most likely, to review electrical engineering projects. Ken developed enduring friendships with students as well, including Tom Killian. Tom went on to Princeton with Ken and had a distinguished physics career of his own.

FIGURE 2-6:   Dorm Life — Water Fight MIT

As with any college full of young men, there were hijinks and misadventures. A huge water fight involving fire hoses did some damage to the dorm in 1925. The school paper, *the Tech*, also mentioned the Dorm Goblin in February 1925, describing the curious incident of a dorm resident returning to his room to find that the front door had disappeared. Ken would have been too busy to participate but must have had some memorable times with his classmates.

The roaring twenties were a time of optimism and hope. Students at MIT could see firsthand that their opportunities were nearly boundless. The 1924 MIT yearbook notes that six members of the class of 1893 were already millionaires. As loyal alumni, they funded the construction of a much-needed dormitory, "93 Hall."

At GE Schenectady, Ken had gotten to know the director of the research lab, Willis R. Whitney, as well as chemist Howard Jones and physicist Saul Dushman. Ken had seen some things at GE (presumably management issues) that he did not like, and thus declined the offer of an engineering position there. Instead, he decided to pursue a PhD in physics. "If you're interested in physics, Princeton's the place to go," they told Ken.

KENNETH TOMPKINS BAINBRIDGE

New York, N.Y.
"Ken"; Born July 27, 1904; Prepared at Horace Mann School; Cooperative Course in Electrical Engineering; Aeronautical Engineering (3,4); Electrical Engineering (3, 4); Beaver; Tau Beta Pi; Class Secretary (2); Class Treasurer (3); VooDoo (Business Associate, Board) (1); Finance Committee (3); Entered Freshman Year

FIGURE 2-7:   Graduate MIT 1926

Princeton

1926-1929

Historic campus motto:
Dei Sub Numine Viget
Under God's Power She Flourishes

Current informal motto:
Princeton in the nation's service
and the service of humanity

CHAPTER 3

Princeton

Princeton was a logical choice. Ken had met Karl T. Compton, the head of the physics department at Princeton, while Compton was working as a consultant at GE on the conduction of electricity in gases. So finally, with his best friend Tom Killian, Ken applied to Princeton. They were both admitted. Andrew Fleming West, a classicist, and dean for 27 years, pretended to be shocked. In a little dig at the "techies" from MIT he said, "You're nice boys but it's too bad you never went to college." Ken's subsequent immersion in the more traditional college atmosphere at Princeton made up for his tech and industry background.

FIGURE 3-2: "You're nice boys, but it's too bad
you never went to college" Dean West

Princeton's physics department was strong, with Karl Compton;[5] Ken's faculty supervisor, Henry DeWolf Smyth;[6] Allen G. Shenstone, Louis A. Turner, and Charles Zahn. The 1925 hiring of these scholars sparked new research on nuclear physics. Smyth had been one of Karl Compton's students and was promoted to associate professor in 1929, and full professor in 1936. A U.S. National Research Council Fellowship enabled Smyth to go over to the Cavendish Laboratory at the University of Cambridge in England. He worked with Ernest Rutherford and earned a second PhD. His experience no doubt smoothed the way for Ken, who would also win a fellowship to the Cavendish Lab.

FIGURE 3-3:   Ken's PhD supervisor, Henry DeWolf Smyth

The physics department already had two faculty members with Nobel prizes when Ken arrived. Bridging the generations, William Francis Magie, founder of the American Physical Society in 1899 and acting department chair in 1926, was the first professor of physics at Princeton University. He was also author of an early physics textbook (1911) and the Dean of Faculty for two decades.

Karl Compton, the department chair (1929–1930), represented the new physics program in a number of lectures for the public. In 1927, he highlighted the value of physics training for workers in other fields. He also emphasized the importance of theoretical work that could be done with nothing more than a pencil, a piece of paper, and a brain. Of course, Ken could do that too, but he was exceptionally talented at experimental work, designing, and fabricating new equipment.

Working in the Palmer Lab with Smyth, meeting visitors, and attending lectures, Ken developed connections with students and scientists from various fields that he maintained over his lifetime. These relationships proved invaluable during the war and in his future endeavors at Harvard, the Radiation Lab, and Los Alamos.

It was not all work. Ken and Tom shared a suite near the entrance to the dorm and were often entertaining visitors. One night they liberated the keys to the campus tower and set off the 37 bells of the carillon at 3 AM. Tom Killian went out with visiting southern belle Virginia Brinkley and Ken was paired with her younger sister Helen, who apparently said she was sixteen, but was fifteen. She developed a crush on Ken (despite their age difference) and was disappointed that it did not work out. Helen kept in touch by sending Christmas cards to Ken's family, and then visited them almost thirty years later.

FIGURE 3-4:   Dean Christian Gauss

The campus was noted for parties and debauchery, as Dean Christian Gauss' diary (1926–1929) makes clear. Alumni complained that academics had given way to sideshows as students picked courses that were easy ("roaring guts") and avoided their opposite ("bitch kitties"). They booed and jeered at football games and sang songs laced with profanities and innuendo. Gauss whispered to Edmund Wilson about "students drinking, whoring, gambling ... setting fire to haystacks in the fields and making bonfires on Blair Tower." Their snowballs broke thousands of Gothic windows every winter. Bootleggers set up on adjacent streets to fulfill the student demand for booze — despite Prohibition.

As a graduate student, Ken developed an interest in the study of nuclei, leading to his lifelong interest in mass spectroscopy. He started with a careful look at Arthur Jeffrey Dempster's mass spectrometer of 1918. Dempster had established the basic theory and design of mass spectrometers that is still used to this day. In 1919, Francis W. Aston improved the mass spectrometer design to achieve a mass resolving power of 130 and won the Nobel Prize for his work in this area in 1922.

The work Ken did at GE led to several patents in photo-electrics that would improve movie soundtracks and television many years later. He had also learned the value of rubidium and caesium for photo-electric devices and this experience helped shape the experiments he undertook in the Palmer Lab at Princeton. Ken's interest in understanding the elements and their isotopes led to his lifelong work with spectrometers. He eventually worked with many instruments in physics, including cyclotrons, but spectrometers were his favorite.

He built his first mass spectrometer following Dempster's design but was frustrated by its low power. He redesigned it and built an improved model for his thesis. Ken went looking for Element 87, known at the time as eka-caesium. It was known that a tungsten filament heated to 1200°-1300°K will convert all the caesium atoms that strike the tungsten surface into ions, and Ken was confident eka-caesium would behave the same way. The tungsten filament creates an intense homogeneous source of positive ions he could examine with his mass spectrometer.

He was looking for atomic mass number 223 or 224. The chemical separation of caesium and admixed eka-caesium was made from pollucite and lepidolite ores from Oxford Country, Maine. These were known to be rich in the lighter alkali elements—lithium, sodium, potassium, rubidium, and caesium. Eka-caesium turned out to be very rare, no more than 35 parts

per million in the caesium refined from pollucite, or 7.3 parts
per million for the caesium from lepidolite.

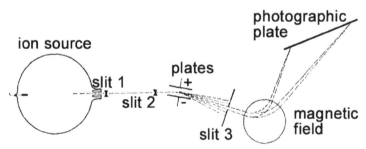

FIGURE 3-5:   Aston's Mass Spectrometer

During his years at Princeton, Ken developed new and improved methods for identifying rare elements and began his
study of nuclei. Ken's mass spectrometer followed Arthur Dempster's design (1918) using directional focusing properties of 180°
magnetic fields; and Francis W. Aston's design (1919–1925)

using a magnetic field to permit a ribbon-like beam of ions with a small range of energies to be spread and focused on a photographic plate. Heavier ions are deflected least.

Ken thought he could do better and did. By 1932 he had built an improved velocity selector model with a resolving power of 600, and precision of one part in 10,000. The ions are made accurately parallel by a slit system and then enter an electric deflector with parallel plates where they are deflected by an angle and spread into an energy spectrum, that for a fixed mass is a velocity spectrum. His spectrometer included a plate with a film record to record the traces of ion impacts. This made it possible to identify different isotopes of an element that have the same nuclear charge but different numbers of neutrons. The same principle was later used to select uranium isotopes.

In 1935–36 he designed and built a double-focusing (electric and magnetic fields were arranged in tandem so that ion beams that emerged from the source slits in divergent directions and with different velocities were refocused) mass spectrometer with a resolving power of about 60,000. He was assisted by Edward B. Jordan, J. Curry Street, H.R. Mimno and the fabricator David Mann.

In the summer of 1927, Ken visited Germany and France, and then returned to England, Austria, and France in 1928. He may have been looking for better sources of element 87 for his research. Pollucite had been found in sedimentary rocks in Germany and Switzerland, while lepidolite with both rubidium and cesium was found in several locations in France. Travel costs may have been met in part with funds from the Charles Coffin Fellowship (1927–1928) and the Class of 1861 Fellowship (1928–1929). MIT alumni and utility executive Alexander Macomber may also have helped out, for he was traveling with Ken. In 1928, they flew from London to Paris. A noisy but remarkable two-and-a-half-hour flight for just £5 5 shillings. No doubt some work was slipped in around the travel and sightseeing.

Element 87 is very radioactive and he could not isolate it. It was eventually found by Marguerite Perey at the Radium Institute of Paris. She called it Francium. Element-87 exists naturally, only as short-lived isotopes from the decay of actinium, Element-89. The longest-lived isotope of E-87 has a half-life of only 22 minutes.

This must have been frustrating for Ken, but learning is not always about the final answer. He had discovered and refined methods for identifying isotopes. He had also learned that his methods could be used to separate isotopes and determine isotope intensity ratios. His development work, the construction and refinement of his mass spectrometer, and other aspects of his research, were also important.

FIGURE 3-6:   Ken's flight London to Paris 1928

Ken presented his oral defense of his dissertation on May 11th in room 222 of the Palmer Lab. The night before, he had been busy at the Graduate College dinner and dance. Ken and Tom had helped plan the event as members of the Dance Committee. Despite his late night out, Ken passed and was awarded a Ph.D. for his dissertation, "A Search for Element 87 by Analysis of Positive Rays" in 1929.

The Roaring Twenties screeched to a halt on October 29, 1929. Wall Street investors traded some 16 million shares on the New York Stock Exchange and billions of dollars were lost, wiping out thousands of investors. By 1932, stocks were worth only about one-fifth of their value before the crash. This had a tremendous impact on students in school, those just graduated, and on university endowments and budgets.

The Market Crash of 1929

Then the floor fell out. On Monday, Oct. 28, the Dow fell 12.8 percent. The next day, Black Tuesday, it lost another 11.7 percent. By the time the bottom arrived, in 1932, the Dow was down 89 percent from its 1929 peak.

FIGURE 3-7:   The Market Crash

Fellowships

1929-1934

Bartol Foundation Building

CHAPTER 4

Fellowships

K en escaped the worst of the Great Depression with a series of fellowships from 1929-1934. He started out with
fellowships from the National Research Council 1929-
1931, Bartol Foundation 1931-1933, and Guggenheim Foundation 1933-1934.

The Bartol Research Foundation

With his National Research Council Fellowships, 1929-1931,
Ken had some freedom to choose where he would go. He considered returning to MIT or going to CalTech in Pasadena but
decided instead to accept a position at the Bartol Foundation at
Swarthmore College, Pennsylvania.

Henry W. Bartol, a member of The Franklin Institute, left the
bulk of his estate to establish the Bartol Research Foundation
under the aegis of the Franklin Institute. Shortly after his appointment as the first director, Dr. F. W. G. Swann moved the
Bartol Foundation from its temporary lodgings in Philadelphia
to Swarthmore College. Here the staff and visiting scientists
could enjoy the benefits of a college atmosphere. Ken spent
three years at the Bartol Foundation and met Margaret Pitkin, a
Swarthmore faculty member there. On September 9, 1931, Ken
and Margaret ("Peg") Pitkin were married in the Church of As-
cension in New York City. Ken's brother Bill was best man, and
Peg's brother Ned "Edgar, Jr." gave away the bride since both her

parents had died. Ken and Peg would remain at Swarthmore until 1933.

FIGURE 4-2:   Peg and Ken at Uncle Jack's Camp 1932

Ken also began a lifelong friendship with J. Curry Street. Street was working with W. F. G. Swann using an ion chamber for the measurement of cosmic radiation. Street then moved to the physics department at Harvard as an instructor in 1932, later becoming department chair, and science advisor to the dean of faculty of the College of Arts and Sciences (1966–1974).

W. F. G. Swann was especially interested in cosmic rays and nuclear physics, so it was a good fit for Ken. Swann had built a Dempster style mass spectrometer, and Ken was able to refine it by introducing a gaseous discharge source with a Wien velocity filter to get much higher resolution. With his photographic detection system, Ken could now establish the relative abundance of isotopes and make more accurate determinations of the masses of nuclei. He was able to make accurate mass determinations of low atomic number elements.

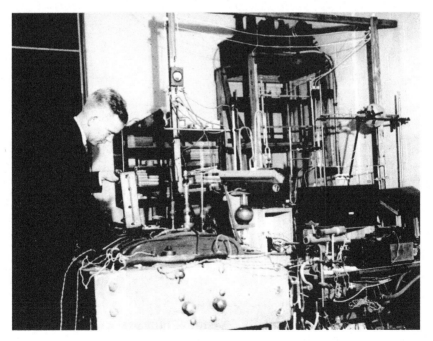

FIGURE 4-3: Ken's Mass Spectrometer at Bartol

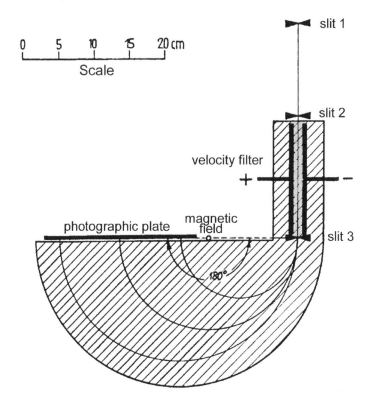

FIGURE 4-4:   Ken's Mass Spectrometer diagram

Ken continued to develop his mass spectrograph, and in 1933 he undertook precise nuclear mass measurements that showed the energy of 17.0 MeV was equivalent to 0.0182 atomic mass units (amu). Aston (in England) and Ken (in the U.S.) had already measured the atomic masses using their mass spectrometers. Ken could now compute the change in mass from nuclear disintegration was 0.018 amu. This verified Einstein's predicted formula $E = mc^2$. That is, the kinetic energy (E) is equal to the relativistic mass (m) times the speed of light (c) squared. In 1934, Ken was awarded the Louis Edward Levy Medal for Physics for this work.[7] It should perhaps also have been selected for the Nobel Prize in 1934.

FIGURE 4-5:   Guggenheim Foundation Award

The Cavendish Lab

As a recipient of support from the John Simon Guggenheim Foundation for 1933 and 1934, Ken joined the Cavendish Laboratory at Cambridge University in England in the summer of 1933. Under the leadership of Lord Ernest Rutherford, Nobel laureate and the "father" of nuclear physics, the Cavendish was the world leader in experimental nuclear physics. In 1919, Rutherford found that nitrogen nuclei ejected what he suspected was a hydrogen atom when bombarded with energetic α (alpha) particles. He named this fundamental particle the proton.

Hine lucem et pocula sacra
From here [we derive] light and sacred draughts

FIGURE 4-6:   The Cavendish Laboratory, Cambridge University, England

In 1932, John Cockroft and Ernest Walton[8] built the first machine that could generate a DC voltage of 280 kilovolts and shoot a beam of protons at speeds high enough to trigger a nuclear reaction. The experimenters closeted themselves in a lead-lined wooden hut in the accelerator room, and then peered through a microscope to look for scintillations due to alpha particles, which they counted by hand. If a zinc sulfide screen hanging on the wall glowed, they added a little more lead – so much for health and safety 75 years ago. The collisions transformed some of the nuclei in the target atoms. They were able to explore the response of the stable lithium seven isotope when it was bombarded: $Lithium^7 + Hydrogen^1 = Helium^4 + Helium^4 + energy$.

Rutherford was very kind to Ken and provided money and space for him. The lab was an engaging and pleasant place to work with many brilliant scientists working on the frontier of physics. Hard work was interrupted for afternoon tea, often poured by Mrs. Rutherford, with treats provided by the researchers. Rutherford sat at the table with everyone for tea, biscuits, and conversation. They discussed physics and science, of course, but also literature and general gossip.

Ken recounted that Rutherford stopped him one day in a corridor to ridicule a suggestion (as obviously impractical) made by a visitor. Leo Szilard had suggested it might be possible to start a nuclear chain reaction based on protons. Szilard went on to envision a much more practical process involving neutrons, which, of course, became reality after neutron-induced uranium fission was discovered in 1938.

Ken had expected to work with Francis Aston, and although Aston was friendly outside the lab, he worked alone. Ken was allowed to see Aston's mass spectrograph but did not get to use it. Aston often had Ken and Peg over for dinner. Ken also went golfing with him and went along with him to the British Open golf tournament.

FIGURE 4-7:   At the Cavendish Lab 1934

FIGURE 4-8:   Talk Softly, The Cavendish Laboratory, Rutherford

FIGURE 4-9:   The Atom splitters - Ernest Walton,
Ernest Rutherford, John Cockroft

In 1934, Ken had time to think and refine his ideas. He developed the design of the double-focusing mass spectrometer he would build at Harvard. His colleagues at home, most likely including J. Curry Street, helped the shop at Harvard start making the parts he needed for the machine following his direction from afar. This saved him a few months when he returned.

At the Cavendish Lab, Ken also met many of the most important physicists of the time. He began a lifelong friendship with John Cockroft (later Sir John). His connections from this time would prove invaluable just before and after the declaration of war.

Ken and Peg lived in a lovely old cottage, but the transition from scholar to housewife must have been a challenge for Peg. Their first child, Martin Keeler Bainbridge, was born in Cambridge, England in 1934. The Great Depression hit them hard and the value of their letters of credit dropped by 30–40%. Ken noted that the family budget was strained after fifteen months in England. It was time to go home.

Ken

Cockroft   Aston   Rutherford

FIGURE 4-10:   Cavendish Laboratory
Researchers, Students and Staff 1934

FIGURE 4-11:   The Bainbridge's home, 18 Grantchester Road

Harvard

═ 1934-1940 ═

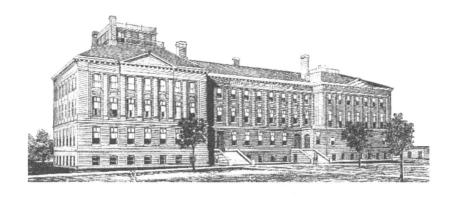

Jefferson Lab
Veritas   Truth

CHAPTER 5

Harvard

The Great Depression had spelled the end, or a bitter interruption, of many academic careers, but not for Ken. He was widely seen as a rising star and received offers from both MIT and Harvard University. He also had an "offer" from Cornell, where Professor R. C. Gibbs would say, "How would you like to come to Cornell? Of course, we don't really have the money now, but we are thinking of you." As a young father, this did not increase Ken's confidence in Cornell as a place with a future.

Harvard it would be. In September 1934, Ken returned to the United States and joined the physics faculty at Harvard University. His Guggenheim Fellowship for 1934 probably provided some funding. In an interview, he said life then was very simple, less complex. There were fewer students by far, with perhaps just twelve grad students in the physics department. The space for study and experimentation grew with the construction of the Lyman Laboratory in the 1930s, including a research library. Ken did not teach many classes and was allowed time for research. In 1939–40, for example, he had to teach a seminar in nuclear physics and classes in X-rays, radioactivity, and nuclear physics (Undergraduate and Graduate) team-taught with Drs. Livingood and Street, and an undergraduate class in electricity, magnetism, light, and atomic physics team-taught with Drs.

Stevenson and Livingood. This left Ken with more time for his growing family and friends.

FIGURE 5-2:   Ken and Percy Bridgman at Crane's Beach 1934

Faculty members also had the responsibility of tutoring students.[9] At times, Ken served as the chairman of the Board of Tutors, organizing tutors and exams. He said there was no carrot attached to the proverbial stick when it came to tutoring. If you had a good student, the tutor might put some effort into it, but there were no grades, so for too many students (and some faculty), he said it was a bore. The intended goal was to build stronger relations between faculty and students, but that was easier said than done. Ken noted, "It's more difficult, I think, in physics, math, or chemistry, than it is in history, or English, or poetry, or art." There, the students already had the "language" to some extent, but in physics and in math, the divide was much greater.

FIGURE 5-3:   Ken's son Martin with Conrad and Phillip Morse 1936

Now and then, there was a bright spot. A. Carl Helmholz was a senior in 1936 and he decided to explore the experimental use of track plates, long before they were used to discover the pi meson. A track plate is a photographic plate with a thick emulsion layer and very uniform grain size. These "nuclear" emulsion plates record the tracks of charged particles passing through them. Ken and Carl got plates impregnated with ^{5}boron and ^{7}lithium salts and found some slow neutrons. That was a rewarding and fun tutorial. Helmholtz would later say Ken was an excellent tutor - letting him choose the topic and helping guide him along the way.

The department wanted to set up new labs to make it easier for students to undertake more advanced experiments. In 1940,

Ken said he was just one step ahead of the sheriff. He would finish a new experiment, get six copies of it set up, and then have to prepare one for next week while giving lectures and running the tutorials.

From 1934 to 1937, Ken made the time to further improve the mass spectrograph he had designed in England. This enabled him to continue his studies of atomic masses. He also began to focus on the structure of nuclear isotopes.

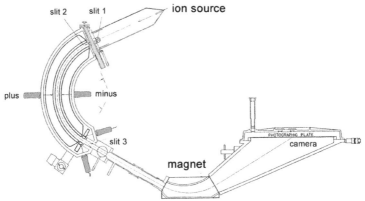

FIGURE 5-4:   Ken's Improved Mass Spectrometer 1938

At the time, the physics department was not sure whether to pursue development of a Van de Graaff linear accelerator or a cyclotron. Fortunately, they chose to build a cyclotron. The cyclotron had been invented at UC Berkeley in 1929 by Ernest O. Lawrence and was constructed by Lawrence and his grad student, M. Stanley Livingston. Cyclotrons proved to be useful in nuclear disintegration experiments in the 1930s. Following the discovery of artificial radioactivity in 1934 by Joliot-Curie, cyclotrons were widely used in producing radioactive nuclei. Some of these were of interest in physics, astrophysics, and nuclear medicine - both in diagnosis and treatment.

A cyclotron is a particle accelerator with charged particles propelled by an alternating electric field between two large electrodes in a constant magnetic field created by two very large magnets. The particles are injected at the center of the magnet and spiral outward as their energy increases. When they reach the rim, a small voltage on a metal plate deflects the beam so it exits through a small gap and hits a target at the exit point at the rim of the chamber or leaves the cyclotron through an evacuated beam tube to hit a remote target. Ernest O. Lawrence was awarded the 1939 Nobel Prize in Physics for his invention.

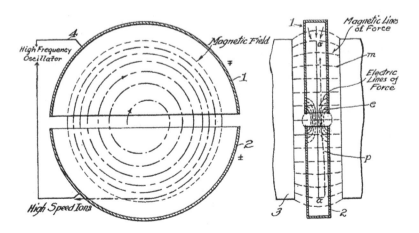

FIGURE 5-5: Cyclotron Patent - E.O. Lawrence

Ernest O. Lawrence at the University of California, Berkeley, was generous about sharing his work and sent drawings of the 37-inch cyclotron they had built. Then, Ken said, "We wanted something a little better, so we decided to go bigger." He estimated the actual diameter of the poles made their new machine a 45-inch, but the diameter of the chamber was only 42 inches. The construction of the cyclotron began in 1936, in the Gordon McKay lab, a wooden World War I. building on the east side of Oxford Street. The magnet weighed 85 tons and could accelerate protons up to 12 MEV (megaelectron-volts).

Harvard's first cyclotron was built on a tight budget. The university put in $25,000, and $30,000 came from individuals and the Associates for Physical Sciences. Materials were scrounged, salvaged, and made by a talented group of faculty, students and workers. The cyclotron was a joint project between the Harvard Graduate School of Engineering, represented by Professor Harry Mimno, and the physics department, represented by Ken and J. Curry Street. Bainbridge and Street were the primary designers and builders. Ken designed and personally drafted plans for the magnet, coils, acceleration chamber, and other accessories.

By 1938 the Harvard cyclotron construction was complete, and Ken was using it to explore atomic physics. One experiment used atomic collisions to change mercury to gold and platinum. One of Ken's colleagues kidded him about violating Pope John XXII's ban on transmutation.

FIGURE 5-6:   Harvard's First Cyclotron, J. Curry Street and Ken

The external beam was used to produce radioactive isotopes for medical purposes. The physics department report states that radioactive materials were supplied to Harvard Medical School, New York Memorial Hospital, and Massachusetts General Hospital. Materials were also sent to Woods Hole Meteorological Station, the MIT physics department, and to members of Williams College and Purdue University. At its peak, the cyclotron was being used by fourteen researchers in various Harvard departments. From 1940 to early 1941, the physics department reported the cyclotron had been in operation for over 1,000 hours. But at the end of this fruitful period, the fate of the first Harvard cyclotron was to change. With so many scientists going into war work, Ken closed the cyclotron down.

FIGURE 5-7:   Inside the cyclotron

FIGURE 5-8:   Harvard cyclotron at work

Ken documented all his projects in great detail. To emphasize this point, he once said, "In the event the cyclotron was ever mislaid, stolen, or borrowed, I knew I could identify it—and later did so at Los Alamos." The operational cyclotron was requisitioned by the U.S. Army in 1943, when it was dismantled and rebuilt at the weapons laboratory. It remained there after the war, never to return to Harvard.

With his work on the spectrograph and cyclotron, Ken explored modifying the naturally occurring abundances of nuclear isotopes. Even before fission was discovered, Ken had been working on separating isotopes. He built up a Hevesy isotope separator and had a theory about a possible way to separate isotopes using a Holweck pump.

When uranium fission was discovered, ^{235}U was found to be the fissionable material. Ken thought he could concentrate it from the natural abundance of just 0.7% with this very efficient pump. The light isotope, the one that was wanted, would congregate at the low-pressure end, and the heavy stuff would be at the high-pressure end. Ken talked it over with Harvard chemists George B. Kistiakowsky (Kisty) and E. Bright Wilson. Wilson developed a more detailed theory of this approach, which was not as optimistic as Ken's preliminary calculation, and he tested it. Kisty had worked with Alfred Loomis, so they borrowed a Holweck pump from him and set it up in the chemistry building. Kisty was put in charge, and he got someone to help him run it. Ken then used his mass spectrometer to measure how much separation it produced with argon isotopes. It came out according to Wilson's theory. Kisty went down to Washington, DC to sell it to the government in 1940. He talked it over with the navy, but they said, "Well, boys, just relax. We've got people working on this sort of thing. You just go back and forget about it." So, they quit work on this project.

Ken had first learned about the rising problems of the Nazis during his time at the Cavendish Lab. Jewish scientists had started to leave Germany and their stories were often grim. He became more concerned after German forces invaded Poland in September of 1939. America was neutral and still harbored a large isolationist streak. The famous aviator Charles Lindbergh was giving non-involvement speeches around the country, including a radio broadcast on October 13, 1939, "Neutrality and War". Ken's work at Harvard went on but it was clear a war was coming.

The
Radiation Lab
1940–1943

The Radar Dome

CHAPTER 6

The Radiation Lab

The Germans invaded Poland in 1939. In 1940, Belgium, Luxembourg, and the Netherlands fell in May and the Allies were defeated by the end of June. The remaining allied forces were trapped on the beach and only a heroic effort at Dunkirk saved them from total destruction. In June 1940, Vannevar Bush, the science advisor to President Franklin Roosevelt; Karl Taylor Compton, president of MIT; and James B. Conant, president of Harvard, presented President Roosevelt with a plan for a National Defense Research Council to oversee scientific research directed toward the impending war effort. Roosevelt quickly approved it. Compton headed up the section, overseeing technologies for detection of aircraft and ships, capabilities that were sorely lacking at the time.

In September 1940, Britain sent the Tizard Mission to the U.S. to share their military secrets and encourage American scientists and engineers to advance the work and develop production systems to manufacture components. The British did not want their major secrets to fall into Nazi hands and be lost to the United States if they were defeated; they were not holding anything back because it was rightly seen as a matter of survival. The technology the Tizard Mission shared included radar, a jet engine, the Frisch–Peierls memorandum on the feasibility of an atomic bomb, designs for rockets, superchargers, gyroscopic gunsights, submarine detection devices, self-sealing fuel tanks, plastic explosives, and much more. The Tizard Mission made it clear that one of the highest priority items was to get more work on microwave radar started in the U.S. The Battle of Britain was underway and better radar could pinpoint attacks, guide defenders, and improve targeting.

John Cockcroft was visiting Halifax, Nova Scotia as part of the Tizard team from England, and he sent a cable to Ken, requesting a meeting in Boston. Ken was up in New Hampshire at the time, but went down to meet him.

Later, Ken met the full Tizard Mission group. When they first met, Cockcroft could not tell him much about the war effort (it was Top Secret), but they all went out to Alfred Loomis' house at Tuxedo Park for an evening of drinks and supper, and no doubt, discussions about microwaves and the application of physics to the war effort.

The Tizard Mission group was touring U.S. companies with electronic manufacturing capability and showed their powerful cavity magnetron to the engineers at the Bell Telephone laboratories in New York. The cavity magnetron was a thousand times stronger than anything available in the U.S. at the time and it allowed radar equipment to be made small enough to fit into an airplane. (Today, cavity magnetrons power the microwave ovens we have in our kitchens.)

Microwaves were clearly going to play a critical role in the war and Compton assigned the task to Alfred Lee Loomis, a tycoon with a private state-of-the-art physics lab and an interest in microwave technology. He also had a working, but weak, radar system. Loomis was appointed the chairman of the Microwave Committee. They knew that microwaves could provide the ranges and accuracies needed to detect aircraft and ships if a sufficiently powerful microwave source could be developed.

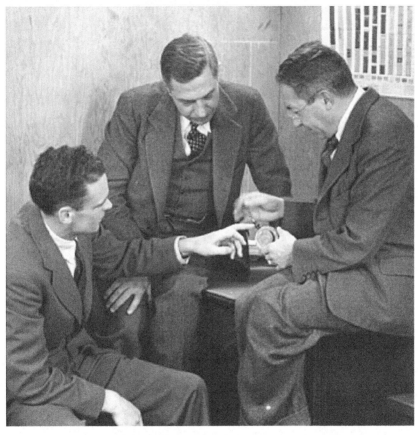

FIGURE 6-2:   The Magnetron Men: E.G. Bowen, L.A. DuBridge, I.I. Rabi

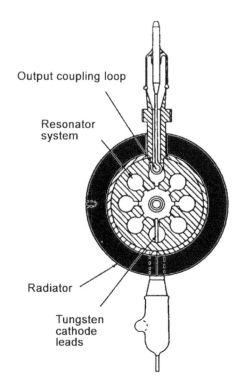

Output coupling loop

Resonator
system

Radiator

Tungsten
cathode
leads

FIGURE 6-3:   Cavity Magnetron Diagram

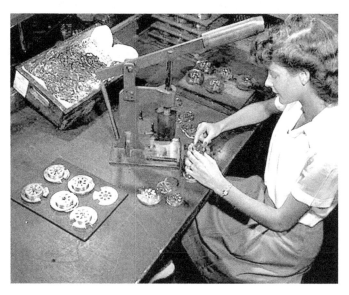

FIGURE 6-4:   Magnetron Assembly

RADAR is an acronym for RAdio Detection and Ranging. The term RADAR was coined in 1939 by the United States Signal Corps as it worked on these systems for the navy. The most basic form uses a transmitted radio signal and a receiver that detects the echoes off any objects in the path of the signal. In the 1930s, eight nations had developed some form of radar. The development of the cavity magnetron in 1940 enabled pulsed radar systems to be used on planes; it could convert DC power to the 10-centimeter wavelengths needed. There are many types of radar, and the Rad Lab would work on more than 100 of them. These included air to surface, surface to surface, surface to air detection, shipboard search radars, air-to-air interception radar, harbor and coastal defense radars, gun-laying radars, ground-controlled approach radars for aircraft blind landing, interrogate-friend-or-foe beacon systems, early warning, proximity fuses, and more.

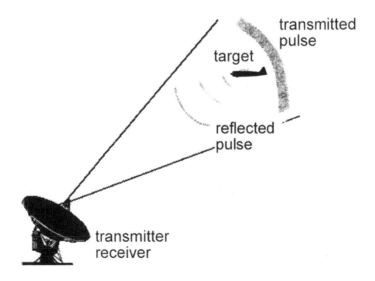

FIGURE 6-5: Basics of Radar diagram

Ernest O. Lawrence was visiting from California and met Ken at Harvard in late September. He asked Ken to walk around the Harvard Yard with him; it was during this walk that he shared the latest news about radar developments. In early October, Karl Compton, the President of MIT, was heading up the section of the National Defense Research Council overseeing technologies for the detection of aircraft and ships, capabilities that were sorely lacking at the time. He asked Ken to come down to Washington but didn't say why. Ken said, "I haven't been cleared yet." Karl replied, "Well yes, you are cleared." Upon Ken's arrival, they went out to the Naval Research Laboratory to see its working radar, good for almost fifty miles.

Lee A. DuBridge, a nuclear physicist from the University of Rochester, was recruited to serve as the first director of the new laboratory. Ernest O. Lawrence was hired, and he recruited Ken. Ken took a leave of absence from Harvard, and started work on what would become the Radiation Laboratory (the Rad Lab) in October. He spent a productive 2.5 years working on this project.

Ken's friendship with the British physicists, especially with John Cockroft, became an invaluable asset. Cockcroft had been involved in the development of the ground-controlled interception stations all along the east coast of England that gave plot positions for approaching German planes —including low-flying planes. Ken went to Washington to meet with industry engineers and managers at Sperry, Western Electric, Raytheon, Westinghouse, and General Electric. Needless to say, his days at GE certainly influenced his opinion of them and how he approached the discussions.

What needed to be done was increasingly clear, but where and how would be the next questions. Ken was asked to find a place to set up this new research operation. For Ken, this was easy; it would be either Harvard or MIT; he knew them both well. They had machine shops, workshops, labs, skilled techs, and were informal enough to get things going without memos and work orders in triplicate.

Karl Compton, the president of MIT, was in Washington, and told Ken, "Well, there must be space at MIT, and if there's not, we can build more. You go down there and look around. See how much space you can get." It wasn't easy. Ken looked at the steam lab, spaces in Building 6, and finally, the lab got a little space in Building 10.

FIGURE 6-6: Radiation Lab Technican

Milton White recalled that there were just three rooms at first, and as staff was added it became increasingly crowded with someone literally in a chair every four or five feet. The din was fantastic. Lee DuBridge had his office in a little glassed-in cube back in the corner where he didn't suffer from all the sound, but when he came out into the office, he routinely placed his hands over his ears.

Alfred Loomis shut down his private lab at Tuxedo Park and moved his people and resources to MIT. He also provided funding for needed equipment and people. Thanks to his deep pockets, items that were needed could be bought and delivered long before a memo could make it to Washington for a government purchase order.

By coincidence there was a conference at MIT on applied nuclear physics in late October 1940. Research scientists from all over the country came for the conference, and many of them were recruited and never went home. (They had to send for their wives and children.) At first, the thought was that only a core group would be housed at MIT, with the rest of the work going on around the country. It was soon apparent that approach would not work, and that the work had to be centralized. Recruiting and hiring at MIT picked up in pace. Then the problem became figuring out where they would all live.

FIGURE 6-7: Radiation Lab Badge

The associate director of the lab, Wheeler Loomis, saw that workers had decent salaries. Ken said there was quite an increase in the number of automobiles on campus almost immediately. In another nine months, there was a great increase in the number of children now that people could finally afford to have them. The Depression had lifted.

Ken's main responsibility during this time was to head the modulator group. Ivan Getting, a Harvard Junior Fellow in Physics, was one of his first recruits. A modulator is needed to generate a short pulse of high voltage for the transmitter tube at the moment of transmission. The radar modulator switches on the anode voltage for the high-power tube for the duration of the pulse.

FIGURE 6-8:   Receiver Room, Radiation Lab, early days

Ken was selected to be the first technical specialist to learn more about radar developments in England, traveling in March 1941 and spending the month of April there. The war and submarine attacks had limited normal shipping, so Ken went over on what he said was a terrible ship, the *S.S. Siboney*. This craft was leased by the government from the Cuban Mail and Steamship Line, originally to get refugees out of Portugal and Americans to Portugal. When the ship stopped in Bermuda, the authorities just took the ship apart, except for people on State Department passports. Ken had one, so he ran around the island all day and had a wonderful time.

Finally, Ken flew from Lisbon to Bristol on a C47 (civilian DC-3) with everything removed from the plane except, as he noted, "the engine, gasoline, and altimeter." This was done to extend the range of the plane to make the 1,500-mile flight. At about 150 mph, it would be an uncomfortable ten hours. Once they got to England, they dropped to near sea level and scooted up the Bristol Channel. The Germans were bombing the railroads outside London, so they stayed in Bath the first night.

His first night in London, John Cockcroft invited Ken and his colleagues to dinner at the Connaught Hotel. They got there before dark, about twilight, and had a delicious dinner, despite the war and the rationing that had gone with it. There was fire-bombing that night, and luckily it was not intense, heavy bombing, but Cockroft still had to borrow Ken's tin hat to go home.

MISSION TO ENGLAND 1941

SS Siboney

FIGURE 6-9a: Ken's Mission to England

Stripped C-47 for the run from Portugal to England

Bristol Channel

FIGURE 6-9b: Ken's Mission to England

Ken then met with the British Royal Air Force chiefs with President Roosevelt's special envoy (Averell Harriman) in attendance. It was at this meeting that they made it clear how important it was to get radio sets and equipment ready for American and British planes. (This was almost nine months before the U.S. entered the war!) The magnitude of the task became evident; to supply just the planes the United States was building for England with radar, identification systems, and radios would take the entire output of the Radio Corporation of America.

Ken toured all the British labs working on radar to meet people and find out what they were doing. John Cockcroft set up the meetings, and Ken had full clearance in order to see everything he could. Since he had been to England before, Ken remarked rather humorously, "If I said I was Bainbridge and I looked like Bainbridge, then I was Bainbridge and I didn't have to have someone trot around with me." One of the most valuable things Ken got was research Wilfrid Bennett "W.B." Lewis had done on the radar cross-section of planes at different wavelengths; no one on the American side had done anything like it. They called them RDF labs (radio direction finding), an old technology without range (distance) capability, to confuse the Germans.

Ken visited groups working on radar to help searchlights find and spotlight planes for anti-aircraft gun aiming, air-interception from plane to plane, and ground-controlled interception. Ken took careful notes on all the wavelengths and whatever else seemed important. Much of this was very valuable because little work like this had been done in the United States.

Ken's also heard about the concept of chaff, dropping aluminum foil strips to confuse enemy radar. The Germans had developed fairly good radar, but chaff could produce enough reflections to make it difficult for them to target aircraft.

Ken was based at the U.S. Embassy, and when he went out on a trip to get information, he was ordered to keep his notes in a money belt. When he got back to the embassy, he went into the code room, removed his money belt, and gave it to the clerk. Later, he would have to come in and transmit the information in code by radio or cable. Non-critical information could simply be put on a returning ship.

Ken returned to the Rad Lab with a great deal of information about what was being done and needed doing. It may have been one of his most important contributions to the war effort, and no one else was so perfectly suited for the task. Ken returned home with a better idea of the work he could do. The trip also helped the Rad Lab recruit E. G. "Taffy" Bowen, who had overseen the airborne interception (AI) radar work in England. This was a very effective direct tech transfer.

The navy would state a problem and then the Rad Lab reps would help define what needed to be done. Lieutenant Commander Stedman Teller decided that fleet security was critical; he wanted the Rad Lab to design something that was narrow beam, could work fairly close to the water, and could pick up incoming planes from distances further than could be visually seen. Ken went down to Washington in December 1941 to discuss it. It was made a bit easier because the antenna could be mounted as high as you could go on the aircraft carrier, so long as it could get under the bridges at major harbors.

The first commercial radar system was placed on the aircraft carrier *U.S.S. Bunker Hill* (CV17) and it was taken to the Caribbean for testing and training. Ken said it was an immediate hit because the pilots in the trial attack run, a big group, took off without realizing their compasses were set wrong. The group had mistakenly started off toward Africa and all would have just dropped in the drink, were it not for the radar showing this. Officers on the Bunker Hill were notified and they reached the executive officer on the *U.S.S. Yorktown*. For some reason they could not reach the planes by radio but sent out a plane that managed to turn them around and get them back to the ship.

Ken said there was a similar case when they were working from the MIT roof. It was a dark, stormy night as a pilot was trying to find the Worcester Airport, but he was way off. He was able to connect with the Rad Lab by radio and they used their radar plot to get him close enough to see the Worcester Airport and land safely.

Ken said he spent most his time on the second-story addition of Building 8, where people could see a 10-centimeter radar with an 8-foot antenna; that is where they tested the aircraft detection radars.

Catherine F. Scott, Ken's secretary at the Rad Lab, said he kept his files in a notebook, like a research notebook — filed chronologically. He carried them around with him when he went to meetings, and the notebooks kept getting more numerous and heavier by the week. When he was away on a trip, she took all the notebooks apart and filed them by subject, alphabetically, complete with an index. He was not exactly overjoyed, but admitted it was not a bad idea.

FIGURE 6-10:   Radiation Lab, later days

Ken had a wide range of responsibilities at the Rad Lab. He was working under the director, Dr. Lee A. DuBridge, and was on the Rad Lab Steering Committee until he left for Los Alamos. The Steering Committee met with the director, associate directors, and the heads of the various divisions. The committee eventually included about twenty people DuBridge thought most capable of helping him, and he relied heavily on them. The committee generally met once a month, at 1 pm on a Saturday, just when the normal work week concluded. The Steering Committee set policy, jurisdictions, hammered out compromises, and made long-range plans. They also worked closely with the

Coordinating Committee to manage the exchange of technical information among the various groups.

This may seem like too many committees, but it was important with so many people working on so many unknowns. Progress in one area could quickly lead to changes in another. Ken was ideal for this because he was an excellent listener, calm and collected, understood the issues well from both engineering and scientific sides, and had a good sense of humor that helped lighten the atmosphere.

Ken started out as the Group Head of Component Development from November 1940 to March 1941. His team worked on pulse modulators, helping to increase the power from ~100 kilowatts to more than 10 megawatts by 1945. Ken served as British Liaison from March to August 1941. He had traveled extensively and met the many English radar development groups as well as the Maud Committee, working on atomic bomb theory. After he returned, he wrote up his trip and moved to Group Head of Systems Development (August 1941–May 1942), and was then moved up to Division S Head for Transmitters from May 1942 until he left for Los Alamos.

The work was intense, and the hours were long. Everything that was done in Ken's office was either TOP SECRET, SECRET, or CONFIDENTIAL. Everything was stamped a dozen times and kept covered up, under lock and key. The document files were kept in a safe. These files were about the various radar projects: the SZBL, SCR 582, SCR 584, and others.

Ken was often traveling and had many visitors. Before he took off on a trip he frequently went into the Rad Lab on Sunday, when it was quiet. He would dictate a great deal of material on the Ediphone (a dictation/transcription machine) to be typed while he was away. Catherine could not always understand what he was saying because he was smoking; when he took a puff and exhaled, he turned his head away from the microphone. She had other science staff check her transcription to catch misinterpretations.

In the early days, Catherine said the Rad Lab was quite informal, just the way Ken preferred it. The dress code was casual, and the people were friendly. The scientists put in a great deal of overtime. If there was a job to do, they stayed, and the support staff stayed to finish it. Everyone knew these projects mattered.

The Rad Lab was working closely with manufacturing companies and people were coming in and out for training and cooperative research. In some ways, it was like a university for microwaves. GE Schenectady was involved in developing the advanced electronic components and systems and had two labs working on radar and taking concepts developed at the Rad Lab into production. Some of the tubes used in the early British radar systems were essentially hand-built and immediately put on a plane for England. Ken also worked well with Raytheon.

Air-to-surface radar played a critical role in the effort to halt shipping losses from German U-boats. Visual intercepts were very difficult, but radar could easily identify subs running on the surface and conning towers on partially submerged subs. The British systems were good but improved with Rad Lab work and manufacturing improvements. Subs had to hide more often and tried to run submerged with snorkels up to provide oxygen for the diesel engines. This dropped their speed from 17 knots at the surface to just 6 knots and impaired their sound detection (sonar) equipment. The Germans developed radar-detecting Metox receivers and these were installed beginning in late 1942. They could detect the 1.7 m waves from the ASV Mark II radar; but they could not detect the more accurate 10 cm ASV Mark III. Allied shipping losses dropped and German submarine losses spiked as the new radar came into use.

FIGURE 6-11:   German Sub, Detected by Airborne Radar

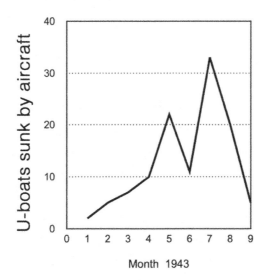

Month 1943

FIGURE 6-12:   Air to surface radar made German submarines vulnerable

The first 10 cm microwave search radar for the U.S. Navy was developed by the Rad Lab and Raytheon in June 1941. With a gyro-stabilized mount, the SG model could detect large ships at fifteen miles and a submarine conning tower at five miles. The SG proved to be one of the most successful radar sets, with the first installation going to sea in April 1942. The carrier *U.S.S. Saratoga* and the light cruiser *U.S.S. San Juan* had the second and third sets.

The 1942 battles in the western Pacific were soon shaped by radar on American ships and planes. The Battle of the Corral Sea (May 4–8) was the first triumph of radar. The American fleet could see the Japanese fleet over the horizon. Planes from the aircraft carrier *Yorktown* struck the first blow. The opposing fleets engaged in a bitter fight. The Japanese light cruiser *Shōhō* was sunk. Two Japanese carriers were damaged and lost many planes, keeping them out of the pivotal Battle of Midway in June.

On the nights of November 14th and 15th, radar helped the battleship *U.S.S. Washington* sink the Japanese battleship *Kirishma* during fierce fighting around Guadalcanal. Radar would play an even more important role in many future sea battles in the Pacific. Air-to-surface radar on PBY flying boat scout planes helped track the Japanese fleet and had a range of 200 miles.

The Rad Lab also worked on Ground Control Approach (GCA) radar. At first, the pilots were not enthused; they were too self-confident and cocky for that, and no one was going to tell them how to fly. But when the chips were down, they appreciated it in soupy weather. In England, they might lift off on a clear dawn and go on a bombing raid yet find nothing but thick fog when they returned; maybe they would try a secondary airfield, and that too might be fogged in. In these cases, GCA radar could quickly become a welcome asset and best friend.

FIGURE 6-13:   Improved radar gave Allied ships the edge in the Pacific — The Japanese heavy cruiser *Mikuma* sinking 1942

Ivan A. Getting would rise to become the director of the Division on Fire Control and Army Radar. His group developed the first automatic microwave-based fire control radar. This system, along with the proximity fuze, enabled England to reduce the impact of German V1 "buzz bomb" missiles. By late August 1944, 70% of V-1s were destroyed by guns along the coast.

Radar operators were also needed. Young officers from the army, navy, and signal corps were taught basic physics and electronics. A dedicated radar school was set up in downtown Boston and the Rad Lab provided instructors and designed the curriculum.

Ken said dealing with the navy was pretty straightforward. "If Admiral Julius A. Furer trusted Sam Tucker, okay, Sam Tucker had the responsibility. So long as he carried it off right, he was backed up." Someone like a Lieutenant Commander could have sizable responsibilities far above his pay grade. The navy officers were typically more technically oriented than people in the army; those in charge at the navy had to know something about complex equipment, electricity, energy, and navigation. The army was more by the "outdated" book. The worst situation could be when the clients were both the army and navy. Conflict between operating systems is called a "purple operation," from the mixture of army red and navy blue. It even had an acronym, JANCFU for "joint army navy combined f—k up."

Ken said the Rad Lab (and later Los Alamos) had many bright and clever workers who had not finished their Ph.D., M.S., or even B.S. degrees, but were put into responsible jobs and did very well. He said the science research supervisors wisely decided to place contracts with the universities rather than individuals. Let the universities sweat it out and leave the fellows who were doing the work alone; keep them away from the contracts, memos, budgets, and negotiations, and let them get the work done.

The Rad Lab had 4,500 workers and a budget of $4 million a month at the end of the war, and had developed more than 100 different radars, trained thousands of operators, published more than 2,000 papers and reports, and supported field upgrades and maintenance of radar installations around the world. By the end of the war, the United States had spent almost $3 billion on radar, half being for equipment the Rad Lab designed. This was more than the cost of the Manhattan Project atomic bomb work.

In the words of Karl Compton, the Rad Lab was "the greatest cooperative research establishment in the history of the world." Ken received a Presidential Certificate of Merit for his work at the Rad Lab. In August 1943, he was recruited by J. Robert Oppenheimer (and General Groves) to work on the atomic bomb at Los Alamos New Mexico.

Ken's mother Mae was now once again volunteering for the Red Cross. She must have been worried with youngest son Don soon to be a lieutenant in the Army Corps of Engineers; her oldest son Bill, a captain in the combat engineers who would land on Omaha Beach on D-Day; and Ken working long hours, soon to move to a secret location out west for two years.

FIGURE 6-14: Mae's Red Cross ID Card 1942

Los Alamos
& Trinity
▬ 1943–1945 ▬

The Main Gate

CHAPTER 7
Los Alamos & Trinity

On his visit to England in 1941 Ken had met and talked with some of the British scientists about their fission work. John Cockcroft invited him to a meeting of the MAUD Committee (a bunch of physicists from Cavendish and London were in on this). Ken had not been cleared and brought into the nuclear project, but he had worked on it on his own at Harvard in 1938. He recalled this discussion in detail.

In 1942, Ken had heard about a project known as Shangri La. No one ever mentioned bombs or uranium, but all agreed it was a beautiful place out in the western United States. In May 1943, Ken was invited to join Robert Oppenheimer's Project Y at Los Alamos. This was under the Corps of Engineers' Manhattan District and Army Brigadier General Leslie R. Groves. (This led to the use of the name "the Manhattan Project for the nuclear research and engineering.") Ken initially led E-2, the instrumentation group, tasked with developing X-ray instrumentation for analyzing explosions.

Norman Ramsey said Oppenheimer sweetened the offer for Ken to go west by telling him about the great fishing. This was in the days of gasoline rationing, and Ken was worried about recreation, particularly fishing opportunities out west that would not require a car. He asked, "How is the fishing at Los Alamos?" Oppenheimer said, "It's great, the Rio Grande is near there." "Well," Ken said, "how easily can you get from Los Alamos to the Rio Grande by bicycle?" Oppenheimer said, "Very easily, it's about a twenty-minute trip." He didn't say, and fortunately Ken didn't ask, "How is it to get back to Los Alamos?" because there was a difference of a couple thousand feet in altitude. Easy coast down, but a long, hard climb back up.

FIGURE 7-2:   The Road to Los Alamos

Ken said the evolution at Los Alamos was comparable to the Rad Lab, but on a much greater scale. Each senior scientist who came out picked four or five of the people he had been close to and trusted, then he would try to lure them out there as a group to help speed up the work.

Ken started recruiting people. He said it was humorous at times and a bit nerve-wracking because he was not supposed to tell them what they would possibly be going to work on, or even where they might be going. Sometimes it was awfully close, but "No one I invited turned me down," he said. It could be a shock for the scientists' wives. An unexpected visitor arrived asking to speak with their husbands in private. After that, suitcases were packed and their husbands left for an unknown destination for an unspecified period of time.

Oppenheimer had been told he would not be able to get to first base without people who were used to dealing with the military. Ken fit the bill, so he was a good candidate. The atomic bomb was such a critical secret that the first thought was that scientists would be invited out in the fall of 1943. On January 1, 1944, they would have to decide whether they would go back home and keep their mouths closed forever or stay on for the duration, in uniform and under military procedure. When the scientists heard about it, they hit the roof; it simply would not work for them to have to wear uniforms and start saluting.

Ken was a key player at Los Alamos. He had been able to discuss fission with the British nuclear team and had also been working on the equivalence of mass and energy. He figured out a way to refine uranium to get the ^{235}U needed for a bomb. Ken also had experience working with the big industrial firms and was knowledgeable in manufacturing and testing from his student days at General Electric.

The managers and builders of Los Alamos faced enormous challenges of support for the many programs involved at Project Y. In addition to providing water, food, and shelter for workers and their families, the engineers and builders had to create lab and manufacturing space, storage space, facilities of all kinds, roads, and much more on a remote mesa in New Mexico. There were also components and equipment coming in from all around the country to be sorted, checked, and prepped. It was remarkable that it went as smoothly as it did. To make it more challenging, most "stuff" could not be shipped direct for security reasons; most first had to go to Los Angeles and then by train and truck to Project Y.

FIGURE 7-3:   Project Y Badge

FIGURE 7-4:   Technical area - Los Alamos

Families were pouring in from around the country. Ken drove out to Los Alamos in the summer of 1943 with his son Martin ("Pidge"). His wife Peg, and daughters Joan and Margi, came by train. Margi had learned to walk on the train. Ken did not get to spend much time with them, but his daughter Joan remembers it as a happy time just the same. The kids had many other children to play with, as well as the surrounding woods and wild areas to explore. Peg became a Cub Scout den mother for Pidge and the other boys.

FIGURE 7-5: The View from Los Alamos

Peg was not an adventure seeker, but she grew to love the southwest, hiking, and the Pueblo people. The great vistas and open spaces were appealing. There were many wonderful people around, like a university campus, including the members of San Ildefonso Pueblo who worked on the site as housekeepers and construction workers.

Ken's daughter Joan fondly remembered their wonderful housekeeper, Juanita Gonzales.[10] Housekeepers were half-day, with the number of half-days determined by the family makeup. (With more children, or if the mother worked, more time was allocated.) Many San Ildefonso men also worked at Los Alamos and Trinity base camp. Po Martinez[11] worked with Ken at the Trinity basecamp.

FIGURE 7-6:   Martin, Peg and Joan

FIGURE 7-7:   Joan, Margi, Ken, Peg, Martin

General Groves tried to get everyone to take Sunday off, and the scientists and families usually did. They went horseback riding, hiking, exploring ruins, with skiing and skating in winter. Ken was a good skater on the iced-over ponds, but Peg wasn't. She preferred to visit the Puye Cliffs and other cultural sites. With some limitations, they could also go to Santa Fe. Ken liked to fish and made lovely fly rods for Joan and Pidge. The lakes and streams of the Jemez Mountains offered excellent fishing with miles of pools and overhanging banks, ideal for trout. The views and quiet serenity were a treat after the intense work. On one camping/fishing trip, the family was sleeping under a three-walled shed when a herd of cattle drifted down the valley. Ken got up and parked the car on the open side to keep the cows out. They would also go down to fish the Rio Grande.

FIGURE 7-8: Spruce Cottage, Bathtub Row

Ken and Peg, with their two small children and a toddler, were assigned one of the "bathtub row" houses rather than one of the recently built houses, some flimsier than others, or apartments. Some people were also living in dormitories, barracks, and later, in trailers and quonset huts. The bathtub row houses had been the homes of the Los Alamos Ranch School masters and teachers. The Bainbridges' home had nice thick walls, a stone fireplace, a bathtub (obviously), and coal stoves that bedeviled most of the wives. One day, General Groves was visiting a bathtub house when one of the wives asked for help with her stove. Being a competent country boy, he agreed. After wrestling with the stove to no avail and getting covered with soot, he left. Electric hot plates started to arrive the next day.

The bathtubs were in high demand and the Bainbridges routinely shared theirs. When Isidor Isaac Rabi won the Nobel Prize in 1944, Kisty made a liquor store run to bring in alcohol for the party. He drove off the road on the way back, and Ken had to rescue him and the alcohol. The giant party also included a roulette wheel, with the winner getting a bath in the Bainbridges' tub.

Ken's daughter Joan said school was fun, with small classes and a very eclectic mix of cultures— with science kids, Hispanic construction workers, and Texas roughnecks. Pidge scavenged electronic parts from the dump and he and two friends built a ham radio and set it up in their treehouse. (This was not well received by the security people.)

On Friday nights, the family could go to the mess hall and have steak and corn dinners — food unobtainable in most American towns due to rationing. The school grew as the Y team grew, eventually adding a high school. One of the treasured breaks was a reserved dinner at Edith Warner's cafe at Otowi. Robert Oppenheimer had known Edith for years and realized the security issues could put her cafe out of business. So, he got approval from General Groves for her to stay open. She and her companion, Atilano "Tilano" Montoya,[12] an elder from San Ildefonso Pueblo, ran the place. Her simple but good food and the quiet setting offered welcome respite from the hubbub at Los Alamos. On Pidge's birthday, Peg arranged for lunch and a chocolate cake there. Scientists who could travel more freely often stopped for coffee and conversation.

FIGURE 7-9:   The bridge to Los Alamos at Otowi Crossing

FIGURE 7-10:   Operators of the Otowi Crossing
Cafe, Edith Warner and Tilano Montoya

Project Y, with the Army chain of command and layers of government bureaucracy, proved a different working environment than the Rad Lab. When compared with the Rad Lab, the scientists were not treated as well at Los Alamos either. Project Y was run by the army and got its money through the army. General Groves was the chief, and Colonel Stewart, based in Los Angeles, handled the mail, paychecks, and appointments. The security people were also army. Ken said there were a few good army people who worked without counting the hours involved; these few saw how effective the informal scientists and academics were and did not try to "shape everyone up." "Their rank did not bother them, except one officer to another, and they could be 'civilians' the rest of the time."

Oppenheimer and Groves set up a governing board for Los Alamos, including Oppenheimer, Robert Bacher, Hans Bethe, Joseph Kennedy, D. L. Hughes (Personnel Director), D. P. Mitchell (Procurement Director). Deak Parsons, Charles McMillan, George Kistiakowsky (Kisty) and Ken were added later.

It became clear that a cyclotron was needed to measure various nuclear reaction cross-sections of interest, and supplement the work already being ably carried out at the Princeton cyclotron. Ed McMillan visited the Harvard lab to see the cyclotron and was given a demonstration. The Manhattan District wanted the cyclotron, and Harvard finally agreed to sell the machine Ken and colleagues had built to the U.S. government for $1, with an informal promise of a cyclotron to replace it when the war was over (a promise eventually fulfilled). Since the atomic bomb project was Top Secret, the purpose of the cyclotron purchase had to be disguised, so medical physicist Dr. Hymer Friedell accompanied the cyclotron (and nuclear physics expert Robert Wilson) out to Los Alamos. The "cover story" was that the cyclotron was needed for medical treatment of military personnel.

In March 1944, Ken became head of a new group, E-9, charged with conducting the first nuclear test. In Oppenheimer's sweeping reorganization of the Los Alamos laboratory in August 1944, the E-9 Group became X-2. Ken was given oversight of the design of high explosive assemblies and responsibility for the preparations for a full-scale test of a nuclear bomb. He said later, "Regardless of whether I was E-2, E-9, P-3, X-2, or some other part of the alphabet, my major duties were largely the same and I was closely associated with Lou Fussell, Phillip B. Moon, Robert W. Henderson, and Roy W. Carlson on detonator development, planning for the test and its instrumentation, and on the problems of design, ballistics, and safing[13] devices for the implosion bomb development." In May 1944, Oppenheimer set up a committee comprised of Richard Feynman, Ken, and several others, to examine the options for all types of nuclear weapons. These questions would include assembly methods (gun and implosion), materials (plutonium and ^{235}uranium), and various forms of matter (metal, hydride, and deuteride). They explored a wide range of problems, from fabrication to calculations. This group began to put the various pieces of the puzzle together. The Trinity test would be an implosion bomb.

Ken's X-2 group was responsible for studying and reporting on the many effects of a field test. The blast, earth shock, neutron and gamma radiations would be studied, complete photographic records would be made, and atmospheric phenomena associated with the blast would be evaluated. The first step was selecting a site for the test.

The site had to be flat, the weather good, with only small and infrequent amounts of haze or dust, not much rain, and relatively light winds. Towns, ranches and grazing lands, and Native American communities should be far enough away to minimize danger from the radioactive byproducts of the explosion.

The test site also had to be within reach of Project Y. Military Intelligence was concerned about security and wanted complete isolation between the site and the activities at Project Y. The military would have to construct the camp and facilities and provide infrastructure for power, water, food, sanitation, and other requirements in a very remote part of the country.

Team members, including Ken, travelled by car to several sites in the southwestern United States. The survey extended as far as San Nicolas Island, sixty miles west of Los Angeles. Low-altitude aerial surveys were made with one or another of the group, including Ken. A great deal of time was wasted in land surveys because the available maps were inadequate; good maps were not obtained in time to be of any use. Maps were requested through the Security Office in June 1944, but many were never received.

FIGURE 7-11:   Site search adventures

In early May 1944, Oppenheimer, Major Stevens, Major DeSilva and Ken piled into two four-wheel-drive 3/4-ton weapons carriers early in the morning and left Los Alamos for the headwaters of the Rio Puerco by way of Valle Grande, Cuba, and Estrella. The snowdrifts over the road were too deep to get through when they were within a few hundred yards of clear sailing away from the rim of Valle Grande. They got stuck but managed to dig out and returned through Los Alamos to take the long way to San Luis and Estrella. Equipped with sleeping bags, food, water and ice for several days, they finally entered the plateau area with the majestic volcanic view of Cabezon Peak in the distance. They slept in the vehicle to avoid the rattlesnakes.

On another scouting trip in September, they were approaching a possible site when a flight of seven B-17 bombers approached and dropped their bombs. Ken commented wryly, "If we had arrived ten minutes later at B-4, it might have been more exciting!"

FIGURE 7-12:   Site search team near miss from bombers

The final location was determined after consulting with Major General Uzal Ent of the Second Air Force on September 7, 1944. He gave the team permission to approach the commanding officer of the Alamogordo Bombing Range, seeking an area within the base perimeter of approximately 18-by-24 miles. The final surveying party for the location of Point Zero and the north 10,000-, west 10,000-, and south 10,000-yard observation posts was aided by the commander of the Alamogordo Air Base. He was an expert on aerial photography, and he had his men photograph the area of greatest interest to create an aerial mosaic map. The photographs were marvelously sharp and detailed; every trail, road, bombing target, arroyo, and even fence lines were identifiable. Ken helped draft plans for the base camp in October. An overview of the proposed scientific measurements at the site was also prepared.

Initially, a major concern was what would happen if the test was a dud or partial explosion. They considered ways that might conserve the radioactive material in water or sand. These did not pan out, so a giant 214-ton metal tank named Jumbo was built and delivered to the site. Kenneth Bainbridge said that, "Jumbo represented to many of us the physical manifestation of the lowest point in the Laboratory's hopes for the success of an implosion bomb. It was a very weighty albatross around our necks." Jumbo was finally abandoned as bomb-grade material became more available, making it less essential to save the nuclear material. Confidence in the ultimate success of the bomb had also increased.

By early 1945, preparations for Trinity were becoming so complex that Oppenheimer appointed the "Cowpuncher Committee" to provide executive direction for the implosion program—to "ride herd" on it. Cowpuncher comprised the Laboratory's top scientific and administrative personnel: Oppenheimer,

Bainbridge, Bethe, Kistiakowsky, Parsons, Bacher, Allison, and
Cyril Smith.

LOS ALAMOS

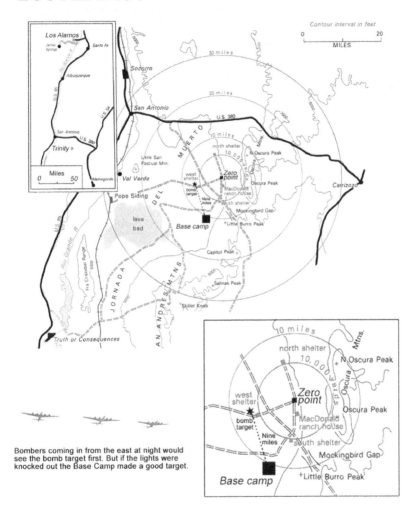

Bombers coming in from the east at night would
see the bomb target first. But if the lights were
knocked out the Base Camp made a good target.

TRINITY

FIGURE 7-13:   Regional Map - Los Alamos to Trinity Base Camp

FIGURE 7-14:   Trinity Base camp

A Little Blast

Pressure for scientific support for other issues drained away staff for the testing program, but Ken's group worked hard to keep up. In the summer of 1944, the idea of a 100-ton high explosive (HE) test shot was considered and decided upon. This would: 1) provide a full dress rehearsal in preparation for the later gadget test, and 2) provide calibration of blast and earth shock equipment. Very little was known experimentally from prior research about potential blast effects created by a few tons of high explosives. The results on blast and earth shock would aid in determining the needed design of structures to withstand these effects on the final test by using scaling factors.

Fortunately, these explosives were not sensitive to mechanical shock. This was confirmed when some boxes fell off a truck transporting the explosives from the rail siding at Pope, and when some boxes fell off the elevator while Ken was making a movie of the HE stack assembly while standing on the stairs above the platform.

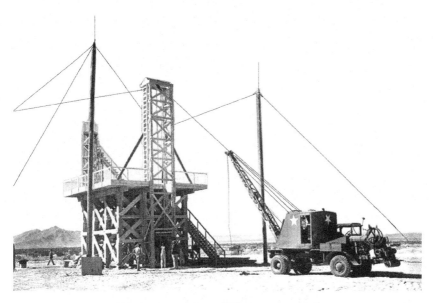

FIGURE 7-15:   100 ton HE test preparation, makeshift elevator to load explosives

The center of gravity of the 100-ton HE test stack was made 28 feet above the ground in scale with the 4,000- to 5,000-ton blast expected at a height of 100 feet for the real event. The stack was treated with a radioactive solution with 1,000 curies[14] of fission products derived from a Hanford slug[15] to simulate, at a low level of activity, the dispersion of radioactive products expected from the nuclear explosion.

For the 100-ton HE test on May 7, 1945, Ken had a team of thirty-three men just working on test evaluation. This test placed heavy responsibilities on younger men, including Special Engineer Detachment members. This required a certain looseness in the organization, but the group functioned as well as could be expected, and developed needed experience for the Trinity test. Ken's team for carrying out the 100-ton HE test, including military personnel, involved more than two hundred men. The greatest strain had fallen on those responsible for timing services, as the trials of signal lines, remote actuating circuits, and test calibrations continued for long periods and at all hours. Ken said, "The complete cooperation and unselfish devotion of all to the work at hand enabled the test to be run on May 7, 1945." The setup was complicated by the ongoing work and layout for the big test.

FIGURE 7-16:   100 ton High Explosive Test Team

The "Arming Party" included Ken, T. R. Head, other scientists, and the army and site security teams. The switches at the command post were not closed until every individual was accounted for and checked in. At 4:37 AM Mountain West Time, the switches were closed.

The detonation of high explosives led to the production of a highly luminous sphere that spread out into an oval form. It was followed by the ascent of a hot column that mushroomed out at a height of about 15,000 feet before drifting eastward over the mountains. The flash and sound were detected sixty miles away at the Alamogordo Bombing Range by an observer who had been notified of the test.

The crater was smaller than expected, just about five feet deep and thirty feet in diameter. Scaling up previous experiments had suggested that 10% of the radioactive activity would remain in the soil within a 300-foot radius after the blast. But only 2% was found, suggesting that simple scaling laws would not properly account for the increase in updraft with a larger blast. The radioactivity in the area was low enough to be safe for several hours of exposure.

Most of the test equipment and many of the cameras worked, but some were not turned on and others failed. On some, the batteries were too weak. Important lessons were learned about the equipment and procedures for testing. One of the most important lessons was the need to set a firm date beyond which further apparatus, especially electrical, could not be introduced into the experimental area.

Those who had no prior experience in field work learned about the difficulties and tribulations (by way of heat and dust) associated with work away from a well-equipped laboratory. Temperatures were often in the 90s during the day, but cooler at night.

The test site also experienced problems with the bombing range. On April 17, 1945, a plane dropped a flare into camp, but it got worse. One of the bomb test targets was less than nine miles from Trinity base and can still be seen on air photos. On more than one occasion in May, the night training bombers coming from the east on their final check flight of thousands of miles (getting ready for the run from Tinian to Japan) mistook the test site buildings for the target. The lead plane on a practice night raid may have accidentally knocked out the generator or otherwise doused the lights at their intended target. The bombers would see the Trinity base camp lights ahead and bomb it instead. For security reasons, they had not been informed of the Trinity base camp.

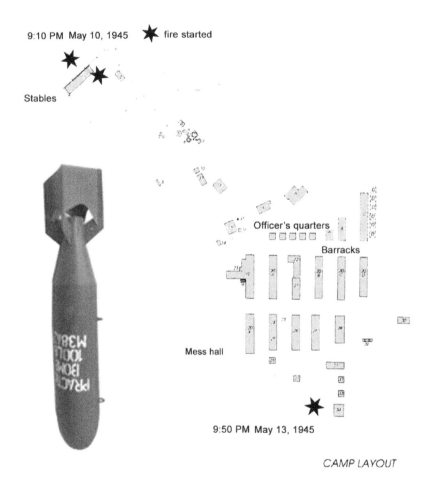

9:10 PM May 10, 1945   ★   fire started

Stables

Officer's quarters

Barracks

Mess hall

9:50 PM May 13, 1945

CAMP LAYOUT

FIGURE 7-17:   Close calls — Trinity Base Camp Bombed

These were sand-filled 100-pound practice bombs with a black powder spotting charge of five pounds. Bombs damaged the stables and the carpentry shop and started a small fire. The bombs also interrupted a nightly poker game. They could easily have killed several people. Ken, only partially kidding, suggested they should have anti-aircraft guns installed at the Trinity base camp.

FIGURE 7-18:   Trinity Base camp with flag

The atomic bomb test could be approached with more confidence after the 100-ton High Explosive shakedown. The calibration of instruments was valuable, particularly for blast measurements, where the 100-ton HE data furnished a more useful calibration point than extrapolation from much smaller shots. The blast effects studies provided good data. George Reynolds, who was working on blast effects, was sent out to Port Chicago, near San Francisco, to study the blast effects of the catastrophic ammunition ship explosion the year before. (On July 17, 1944, this disaster killed more than 300 people, mostly African American sailors and workers, and injured as many more.) From the effects he measured on site, George estimated it had been 1,550 tons of HE; bills of lading later showed it had been 1,540.

The earth shock data gave a reference point that was greatly superior to extrapolations from previous experience. The design of shock-proof instrument shelters could proceed with more confidence. The gaps in equipment and organization pointed out by the test could be corrected, or plans altered, to give a smoother operation for the main event.

A few days after the 100-ton HE blast, while the experience was still fresh in their minds, Ken called an "all hands" meeting in which gripes could be aired, and suggestions made to improve operating procedure. Key suggestions were the need for better roads, the need for more vehicles and better vehicle maintenance, more telephone lines and radios, better support for procurement and supply, and improved living conditions.

It was a rough place to live and work. The hardness of the water was challenging for everyone and a water softener that was installed was too small. The base was finally forced to use U.S. Navy saltwater soap and hauled drinking water in from the firehouse in Socorro. Additionally, the rapidly expanding team required more help at the mess hall to feed everyone. But it was not all work. Ken and his team brought in movies, shown outside if the weather was good, or in the mess hall. A baseball diamond was made, and pickup games were common on Sundays. Soldiers, staff, and scientists all played. Hunting was allowed and both mule deer and antelope showed up on the menu at the mess hall.

The military police put their mounts to good use in polo matches played with a soccer ball and cut-off brooms. There were a few dogs, and they provided some welcome stress relief. The scientists could come and go, but the GIs were stuck. Ken commended Captain Howard C. Bush for doing an excellent job of managing the military men. In addition to security there was a Special Services detachment of about forty craftsman and skilled workers, including cat-skinners, high linemen, carpenters, plumbers, and helpers for all of the specialists. These men were recruited from all parts of the army. Some of the rougher types chose this assignment instead of the brig. As the tension rose, the GIs on the security team had some fist fights. Captain Bush would not interfere unless they started using clubs.

Safety concerns were also addressed, and a less rigid format was adopted. For the final arrangements for July 12 and succeeding rehearsals, and just before the July 16 shot, anyone having legitimate business outside the base camp had free access to all parts of the test area. This was made possible by mutual agreement that respected the problems, wiring troubles, and need for unhampered work to get the job done. As a matter of safety, everyone was asked not to kibitz at the tower during assembly, hoisting, checking, etc., any time after assembly started. Concentration was required and critical.

Ken also took part in a test to see what would happen if the bomber carrying the atomic weapon was strafed by a Japanese fighter plane. A full-scale implosion bomb with an inert core was shot up with 20-mm cannon shells to see what would happen to the explosive-containing casing. The explosive lens assembly did not blow up. Ken and Roger Warner waited for what they thought was a long enough time, and then stepped out of their protective barricade to inspect the damage. As they started to approach, they saw smoke starting to curl out of the holes in the casing and beat a hasty retreat to shelter. Nothing more happened for a long time, so they withdrew to let the bomb sit for a few hours. Later, they did inspect it, and blew it up. It was pretty stable.

Trinity – The Big Blast

The organization chart tells it all: Kenneth Bainbridge, Administrative Head. Overall responsibility: Planning and Coordination. Veto power on suggested experiments. Arming Party. The work schedule was intense. Up at 5 a.m., breakfast, off to work at 6 a.m., early lunch; office work when it was too hot in the afternoon, then back to the test area, returning to base at 5 p.m. After supper every day during the week there would be a session on construction, led by John Williams, who led the very important Services section.

This test involved hundreds of men and scientists from many disciplines— from meteorology to nuclear physics. Ken held one- or two-hour meetings every week for progress reports, scheduling, consideration of new experiments, and troubleshooting.

Work on preparations for the atomic test had continued apace at Y and at Trinity. Much had to be done at the site to get it ready, and the Y group at Los Alamos was working hard to prepare the elements for the bomb. The preparations for the bomb test increased in intensity starting in March, when a July 4 date was set for the test. In the final two weeks, about 250 men from Y were engaged in technical work at Trinity, and many more contributed to theoretical and experimental studies at Y and in the construction of equipment. The difficult work of providing wiring, power, transportation, communication facilities, and construction for the test was getting done, despite the summer heat and crowded facilities.

An implosion bomb design had been chosen because it required only 13.7 pounds of plutonium, compared to the 141 pounds of enriched uranium used in the bomb dropped on Hiroshima. The entire Los Alamos laboratory was reorganized in 1944 to focus on designing a workable implosion bomb. A small spherical core of plutonium would be surrounded by high explosives that would produce a compressive wave when they were detonated. This explosive force was focused inward and compressed the plutonium core to several times its original density, making it supercritical. It would also activate a small neutron source at the center of the core, which would assure that the chain reaction began in earnest.

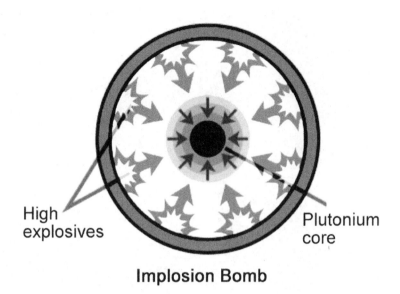

Implosion Bomb

FIGURE 7-19: Implosion Bomb Diagram

The assembly of the High Explosive (HE) charge in the case for the Trinity bomb was preceded by tests at Site Y. These preliminary tests were undertaken to study the best method of loading components and the effects of transportation over less than smooth roads to the test site. Castings for the final assembly were carefully inspected and only the best were selected. On Thursday the 12th, the assembly of the charges began, and by mid-afternoon, the Trinity HE was complete. On Friday, the assembly of the bomb began at the tower. The sphere was transferred from the truck to a cradle, then the active material was installed, and finally, the HE team installed their charges. On Saturday, the bomb was lifted onto the tower. For Sunday, July 15, the schedule read "Look for rabbit's feet and four-leaved clovers. Should we have the chaplain down here?"

FIGURE 7-20: The Gadget - Implosion Bomb

Amid the last-minute frenzy, time had to be found for the many distinguished visitors who had worked on, or were arriving for, the test. These included many observers who had played a critical role in the physics research leading to the bomb and the development of Los Alamos and Trinity. They included Vannever Bush, James D. Conant, I.I. Rabi, Major General Leslie R. Groves, Enrico Fermi, Ernest O. Lawrence, Sir Geoffrey I. Taylor, Sir James Chadwick, and others.

Experiments, cameras, and instruments for the big event were designed to obtain measurements on blast, as well as optical and nuclear effects and characteristics. Another test was a detailed study of the function of the bomb components, design, and detonators. Ken's least favorite measurements were on the simultaneity of detonation of the high explosives. This made this "test" bomb more complicated than the final "production" bombs. It also increased the risk of a possible detonation from an electronic surge picked up from lightning strikes on monitoring and communication wires. No wonder he was concerned.

FIGURE 7-21:   Hoisting the Gadget

There would also be monitoring to understand atmospheric spread of nuclear material. For this, a sample of the earth in the crater would need to be collected as soon as possible following the bomb's explosion. Various aerial collection methods were considered and rejected. Finally, lead-shielded tanks were built. Two were supposed to be finished, one for the reconnaissance and one as a potential rescue vehicle. On the test day, only one was working, and thankfully, it did not need to be rescued.

Ready

FIGURE 7-22:   The Tower with Gadget Set

Tension and excitement were building as the time approached and the bomb was mounted on the tower. The base camp was overwhelmed with people who were working on the test or had worked on the bomb at Los Alamos. Idle watchers were required to go to Compagna Hills, about twenty miles from Point Zero. David Dow oversaw these observers and had a shortwave radio to follow the final countdown.

The frequencies used were meant to be different from any licensed radio stations, but unfortunately matched KCBA in Delano, California. As Sam Allison went through the countdown, it was muddled with "the Voice of America" program for Latin America, "the National Anthem" and Tchaikovsky's "Serenade for Strings."

The team's FM radios at several guard stations, Trinity base camp, and in many Jeeps and cars were ineptly assigned the same frequency as the one used in the railroad freight yard in San Antonio, New Mexico. Trinity teams heard them, and they heard Trinity communications.

Ken was furious when he heard gossip that the atmosphere might be detonated. This had been discussed at Los Alamos and quashed by intensive studies. It was thoughtless to bring this up as a table-and-barracks topic around soldiers unacquainted with nuclear physics.

The stage was set, and the first possible time for the detonation of the real bomb was planned for 2 am on July 16, 1944. The Arming Party arrived at Point Zero before 11 pm on July 15 and attached the cables to the bomb. It was another stormy night with sporadic rain, and at midnight, the first scheduled time had to be canceled due to the weather. Zero time was reset for 4 am, and then it too was washed out. Lightning was reported at the base camp about nine miles away and six miles to the south. This was a risk of uncertain proportions. Ken noted that this enlivened the conversation because so many wires from the site extended six miles or more and ended at the tower.

Finally, just before 4:45 am, Ken got an updated weather report and a prediction that the 5:30 am weather conditions would be acceptable. The goal was, if possible, to avoid heavy fallout on towns, pueblos, or grazing land. Although the scientists and meteorologists had wanted to postpone the test, Groves wanted it done in time for the Potsdam Conference, where President Truman would meet with Stalin and Churchill. The meteorologists would have preferred no inversion layer at 17,000 feet, but they decided that while it was not good, it was not bad enough to require another delay. The biggest concern was the direction the wind would carry the radioactive fallout. Ken called Oppenheimer and General Farrell, and with their agreement, the test was set for 5:30 am.

Ken, George, Kisty, and Joe McKibben had spent the night at the tower. Joe had fallen asleep under a tarp but was awakened by light rain.

Ken returned to the base of the tower and threw the special arming switch. Until this switch was closed, the bomb could not be triggered from the command center six miles to the south. The final task was to switch on a string of lights on the ground that were to serve as an "aiming point" for a B-29 practice bombing run. The Air Force wanted to know what the blast effects would be like on a plane 30,000 feet up and some miles away, simulating a bomb drop and scramble. Ken switched on the lights.

Ken unlocked the master switches and then the three physicists high-tailed it for the Command Post. "We got to South 10,000 (the control bunker) at 5:10, and that was the time I needed to throw the first switch," McKibben recalled.

Donald Hornig, one of Ken's top students from Harvard, took his place near McKibben at the abort switch. Hornig's job was to stop everything if the detonation circuit faltered, in hopes of saving the first precious plutonium from the Hanford works.

At T minus 20 minutes, the timing sequence was started, then a more precise automatic timer took over. In the final seconds, another circuit sent out the electronically timed signals needed by many of the special instruments.

FIGURE 7-23: The Command Bunker at South 10,000

At T minus 30 seconds, Ken left the south command shelter and found Bill Elmore twenty yards away. They put their welder's goggles on and laid down. Ken looked in the direction of Little Burro Peak.

Detonation

The bomb detonated at 5:29:45 am Mountain Standard Time. Ken felt the disturbingly warm heat on the back of his neck; the light was much more intense than predicted. When the reflected light diminished, he turned and looked directly at the fireball through his goggles. A little later, he was able to remove his goggles and watch the fireball continue to rise. He said it grew to a radius of about 300 yards, until the dust cloud growing out of the skirt almost enveloped it. The neck narrowed, and the ring and a fast-growing pile of matter above it rose as a new cloud of smoke, carrying a convection stem of dust behind it. The stem appeared twisted, like a left-handed screw. The cloud of smoke surrounded a faint purple haze and rose until the top reached 1.5 km. No one who saw it would ever forget what he called the "foul and awesome display."

FIGURE 7-24: Trinity Explosion 25 milliseconds

FIGURE 7-25: Trinity Explosion 8 seconds

Ken had a feeling of exhilaration that the complicated "gadget" had gone off properly. This was followed by a feeling of deep relief as he realized he would not have to climb up on the tower to determine what had led to a misfire. After the blast wave passed, he got up and congratulated Oppenheimer and the others nearby on their success. He finished by looking at Robert and saying, "Now we are all sons of bitches."

The fallout plume generated by the blast at the Trinity site moved northeast, creating the biggest radiation doses in Torrance and Guadalupe counties. Lincoln, San Miguel, and Socorro counties were also affected. The radiation effects downwind were downplayed at the time.[16]

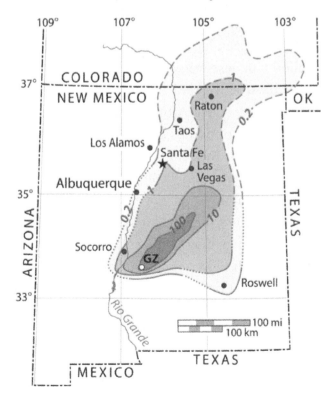

Fallout map

FIGURE 7-26:   Fallout from Trinity

A Needed Break

After working around the clock for almost 5 years, the success of Trinity was a relief. Ken needed a break. The first step was a fishing trip with John Williams to the Rio Grande. He would return to Los Alamos to write up the project, complete analysis of study data, and prepare to leave in the fall.

Aftermath

The Trinity test led directly to the bombing of Hiroshima on August 6th and Nagasaki on August 9th. These resulted in a great loss of life and terrible suffering for the residents of those cities. It is estimated that as many as 200,000 people were killed by the blast and long-term impact of radioactive material.

Sixty-six Japanese cities had already been bombed with high loss of life. From January 1944 to August 1945, 157,000 tons of bombs were dropped on Japanese cities, several hundred thousand people had been killed, and fifteen million of the seventy-two million Japanese were left homeless.

The most destructive raid was a March 9, 1945 attack on Tokyo. The United States Army Air Forces firebombing raid dropped 1,600 tons of bombs from 279 Boeing B-29 Superfortress heavy bombers. The raid burned out much of eastern Tokyo and killed as many as 100,000 people. The Air Force lost 14 aircraft and 96 airmen.

Planners estimated that if Allied forces landed and fought their way across Japan, they would suffer between 1.7 and 4 million casualties, with between 400,000 and 800,000 dead. Japanese fatalities would range from 5 to 10 million. Some argued it could have been settled without the bombs, but Ken did not. However, seeing the impact of the bomb at Trinity, and in Japan, marked the beginning of his dedication to ending nuclear weapons tests and efforts to maintain civilian control of nuclear energy.

FIGURE 7-27:   Robert Oppenheimer and Brigadier General Leslie Groves

Oppenheimer and Groves

The atomic bomb program was a success thanks to the un-likely partnership of J. Robert Oppenheimer and General Leslie Richard Groves. No two men could have been so different and worked together as well as they did. Their mutual admiration enabled them to work together on this very stressful and de-manding project with very little conflict. Without them, the war would still have been won - but it may have taken many more months and cost thousands of lives.

Oppenheimer was a theoretical physicist and innovative thinker without a shred of lab skills. He had a remarkable ability to see what needed to be done next. He was an excellent and engaging teacher. His people skills were a mix of great empa-thy, charm, and at other times, total ineptitude. He suffered from anxiety and depression at times and shrank to a weight of just 115 pounds[17] on a five-foot-ten-inch frame. He was slow to make critical decisions and had little administrative experience. But he was excellent in meetings and proved able to inspire the best from men and women on one of the most intense and larg-est projects of the war. He was very good at explaining complex issues (this had gotten him the job) and identifying what needed to be done. He was also good at picking people who could make up for his weaknesses, including Ken. Ken's calm and cheerful nature, skill as an experimentalist, experience with industry, and ability to work with the military made him an ideal choice.

Asked about his feeling about General Groves, Oppenheimer once said, "Groves is a bastard, but he is a straightforward one." After the war, Oppenheimer had his security clearance taken away during the "Commie" witch hunts. He never fully recovered but led the Institute for Advanced Science at Princeton successfully for many years. He died in 1967.

Groves was a military man— solid, square, tall, and heavyset. He proved able to grasp the science and engineering issues and got things done. He could make even the hardest decisions quickly. He had finished supervising the construction of the massive Pentagon building before he reluctantly took on the bomb project. He was gruff, critical, sarcastic, and almost never complimented anyone. He had a seemingly inexhaustible well of energy as he travelled from Los Alamos to Hanford (plutonium refining), Oak Ridge (uranium refining) to Berkeley, Washington, DC, and all the other labs and companies working on aspects of the bomb. He wrote countless letters and was on the phone much of the time. He characterized the science group at Los Alamos as "the largest collection of crackpots ever seen." But he was able to select and work well with a Jewish physicist with historical liberal connections. He had to override many objections to get, and keep, Oppenheimer.

After the war, Groves received the Distinguished Service Cross and promotion to Major General - over objections. He had hoped to be the Corps of Engineers Chief Engineer, but when he met with General Dwight D. Eisenhower in 1948, he was told it would never happen. The complaints against him for rudeness and self-promotion had killed his chances. He resigned and worked for industry. He died in 1970.

Their secretaries also deserve much greater recognition. This was the time before easy record keeping and communication. Handwritten notes and audio tapes had to be typed with carbon paper, checked, and sent. The fax machine would not arrive until 1955.

Both men had remarkable women as their administrative assistants. General Groves relied heavily on Jean O'Leary, who had worked with him since 1941. She was in on all meetings, took notes on calls, and protected Groves from bothersome visitors. She was given considerable power and authority and was often referred to, with respect, as Major O'Leary. If Groves had been killed, she would have been the only one who knew what was going on across the many labs and sites.

Oppenheimer had the equally skilled Priscilla Green (later Duffield), borrowed from E. O. Lawrence's lab at UC Berkeley. She was paid just $250 a month. When she married and had a baby, her place was filled by Ann Wilson from Groves' office. Both women provided essential support for Oppenheimer.

Harvard

1945-1975

CHAPTER 8

Harvard

In 1945, even when he was down at the desert test site most of the time, Ken was still thinking about his work at Harvard. When he returned to Los Alamos from the Trinity site, perhaps once a week; he would see his family, go to meetings, and perhaps spend a day dealing with business. He also sent letters back to Harvard, encouraging the university to think about, and prepare to act on, hiring choices after the war.

After the successful bomb test, the scientists could write about appointments and research directions without having to go through so much security and censorship. Ken became even more active, knowing that key people were going to be available. He remembered writing a letter that said, "I don't care what else happens, get Ed Purcell! You can do all you want at figuring about Schwinger and other people but get Purcell."

They got him. Edward Purcell had been Ken's first doctoral student at Harvard and worked at the Rad Lab. He returned to Harvard as an Associate Professor of Physics, then Professor of Physics from 1949–1960. In 1951, he was elected to the National Academy of Science. He won the Nobel Prize in 1952 for his studies of nuclear magnetic resonance. At Harvard, he was a Senior Fellow from 1950–1971; Gerhard Gade University Professor from 1960–1980; and Emeritus Professor of Physics from 1980–1997. A solid choice indeed.

Ken was the recipient of two letters of commendation from General Leslie R. Groves for his work on the Manhattan Project and the Presidential Certificate of Merit for his services as staff member of the MIT Radiation Laboratory.

Ken returned to Harvard in the late fall of 1945. He had many ideas about the directions for future research, and perhaps more importantly, the best way to teach nuclear physics. In recognition of his work, he was elected a member of the National Academy of Science in 1946.

Research

Ken had made plans for work after the war, and had money to support his research, thanks to President Conant's foresight. At first, Conant had wanted to pay the salaries of everyone from Harvard who was working on the war effort. The millionaire Alfred Loomis may have planted the idea, as he had helped pay people for research before and during the war. Conant was going to just "give" the scientists to the United States government with Harvard paying their salaries. Ken thought the powers that be in the Harvard Corporation must have said, "Mr. Conant, you're a bright boy, but you're crazy this time." So, Conant let the government hire the researchers. But if the government job did not pay the full Harvard salary, the university would put in money to bring it up to 80% of their compensation package. The brilliant idea Conant had was to put the salaries of the Harvard people who were being paid by the government into a fund for research after the war. This funding enabled researchers to get started right away.

Ken first started work on a new cyclotron to replace the one that went to Los Alamos. In 1945, Harvard University set aside $425,000 to expand research facilities in Nuclear Physics. This was not enough to fund the construction of both the new cyclotron and a new laboratory building, but the Office of Naval Research finally provided funding. The loss of Ken's cyclotron to Los Alamos during the war had not been forgotten, and E. O. Lawrence suggested Harvard should get a replacement, as agreed upon during the war. Eventually, a price for the Harvard cyclotron was set, and working with Harvard President Conant, Ken got $250,000.

This helped pay for parts of the new cyclotron, department expenses, and helped start a nuclear physics program in the medical school. Added funding for construction and research came primarily from defense contracts. The new building was originally called the Nuclear Laboratory.

Ken soon handed the cyclotron project to the newly recruited physicist Robert R. Wilson in 1946. Wilson was new to the physics department but had worked on cyclotrons at Berkeley and served as head of the cyclotron group at Los Alamos. In 1948, after Wilson left, Norman F. Ramsey took over. The design had been completed before the discovery of the pi meson, but sadly, when it was finished in 1949, the energy of the synchrocyclotron turned out to be just below that required to produce pions.

FIGURE 8-2:   The 650 ton Harvard Cyclotron 1949
Lee Davenport and Norman Ramsey

During construction of the cyclotron, Ken insisted to his students that it was for nuclear research and not for medical work.

One of his students, David Bodansky, recalls him saying, "There will be no rats running around THIS cyclotron." However, the first experiment was medical.

The cyclotron was used for a variety of experiments and gradually more and more medical work. It was upgraded in 1955 from 90 to 165 mega electron volts. The operating life was extended when it became a facility for research on the use and clinical applications of the highly focused proton beam, working with staff from Massachusetts General Hospital. The idea of using protons in medical treatment was first suggested in 1946 by Ken's colleague at Harvard, physicist Robert R. Wilson. The cyclotron remained in use for 55 years, retired in 2002.

In his fundamental research, Ken built balanced ionization chambers to determine changes in the lifetimes of several long-lived isomers.[18] This offered new insight into how isomers decay by internal electron conversion when their atoms are differently bonded chemically or are subjected to physical compression. He also designed and built an elegant double-focusing electron spectrograph.

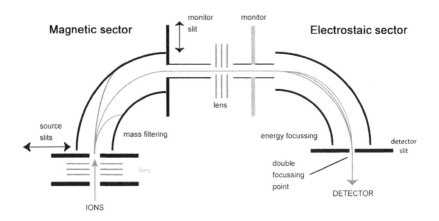

FIGURE 8-3:   Double-focus mass spectrometer diagram

In 1962, the Cambridge Electron Accelerator (CEA) was completed. In the accelerator, electrons whirl around on a constant orbit of 236-foot diameter between a series of 48 strong-focusing magnets. The accelerator tunnel and the powerhouse are connected by four radial tunnels. Professor Livingston noted that the electron accelerator is not properly an "accelerator" in the normal sense of the word. An experiment may start with electrons at 0.99 the speed of light and increase the velocity to 0.99999 the speed of light—not too great a change in percentage terms; what does increase dramatically is the energy and the mass. At the beginning of an experiment, a beam of electrons may have a rest energy of 1/2 million electron volts; it is directed through a linear "pre-accelerator" where the energy is increased to 20 million electron volts. Then, in the accelerator proper, the energy can be raised to the maximum of 6 billion electron volts.

The strengths of the physics department included experimental and high energy physics.

A rest

Ken was due for a sabbatical[19] in 1941, but by then he had left Harvard for the Rad Lab. This sabbatical then became due when he returned from the war, but he could not take it because work was pressing. In 1951, he was finally able to take a full-year sabbatical. He spent half a year doing research at the Brookhaven National Laboratory in Upton, New York, and then went to the California Institute of Technology in Pasadena. There he would write up the work he had been doing over the previous six months. He would return to Brookhaven for additional research. On sabbatical in 1960 he and Peg went to Europe.

FIGURE 8-4:   Ken and Peg Greece 1960

Teaching and administration

Ken had devoted much of his energy just after the war to thinking about how the Harvard physics department should be

organized and how nuclear physics should be taught. He was particularly interested in building an advanced laboratory in nuclear physics for graduate students. The GI Bill enabled many more people to attend universities and the number of graduate students in physics was far greater than it had been before the war. Nuclear physics had gained new visibility and popularity from its contributions to winning the war. Students gained their first experience in activities that prepared them for research in experimental physics in Ken's meticulously designed and documented demonstration labs.

The experiments Ken set up for the students ranged from a replica of J. J. Thompson's positive ray apparatus (a precursor of mass spectrographs) through a bent crystal X-ray spectrograph, a 180-degree beta ray spectrograph using the then-new technique of Nuclear Magnet Resonance for field calibration, and the analysis of tracks in photographic emulsions to identify muons. The department continued its commitment to high school physics education with the program "Harvard Project Physics".

While Ken was out at CalTech on sabbatical, he got a letter from Provost Paul H. Buck saying he would like Ken to consider becoming the next Physics Department chair. Ken agreed, but set a limit of three years, and served from 1952 to 1955. During his tenure he was responsible for the renovation of the old Jefferson Physical Laboratory and established the Morris Loeb Lectures in Physics.

Being department chair is an honor, but also a burden. The job is jokingly equated with the difficulty of herding cats. Managing highly intelligent, focused, willful faculty can be a challenge: it requires a great deal of tact, listening skills, clarity in communication, empathy, steely determination, and a sense of humor. Ken was well-suited for the task, but it took time away from his own work.

FIGURE 8-5:   1954 Horace Mann Alumni Award

One of the most important but unsung efforts a scientist (and department chair) makes is how they select, mentor, and support students and incoming faculty. The choice of faculty is particularly important since their roles can be a 30–40-year commitment. Working with faculty search and selection committees can be aggravating but is essential. Students also benefit from mentoring and support, and they are a professor's legacy.

The physics department faculty that Ken helped select and recruit were conducting important research: Julian Schwinger (1945–1972), Norman Ramsey (1945–2010), and many others. Nine Nobel Prizes in Physics have been awarded to Harvard scientists.

Ken was always concerned about clarity and improving teaching in the department. As department chair in 1953, he guided the phase-out of Physics II, long considered one of the college's most difficult courses. Faculty members teaching this fundamental course felt students were being rushed through it at a speed that allowed only the more brilliant to thoroughly assimilate the tremendous bulk of subject matter. Physics II was replaced with a three-semester course covering roughly the same material.

Ken was the Leverett Professor of Physics from 1961–1975, and he devoted much of his time to improving the graduate student advanced laboratory in physics. As a teacher, he was the author of several courses in the Harvard curriculum that incorporated new materials and methods. Edward Purcell, first his student and then colleague, said, "Even in recent years, when materials in experimental physics were changing very rapidly, Ken was keeping up with it and designing courses around it." This course continues to this day.

PHYSICS 191: Advanced Laboratory

Students carry out three experimental projects selected from those available, representing condensed matter, atomic, nuclear, and particle physics. Included are pulsed nuclear magnetic resonance (with MRI), microwave spectroscopy, optical pumping, Raman scattering, scattering of laser light, nitrogen vacancies in diamond, neutron activation of radioactive isotopes, Compton scattering, relativistic mass of the electron, recoil-free gamma-ray resonance, lifetime of the muon, studies of superfluid helium, positron annihilation, superconductivity, the quantum Hall effect, properties of semiconductors, and plasma physics. The facilities of the laboratory include several computer-controlled experiments as well as computers for analysis.

Ken was a demanding but gentle teacher and boss. He was very supportive of his students and worked hard to find them good positions after they graduated. Higgins Professor of Physics Sheldon L. Glashow recalled a time when, as one of Ken's graduate students, he was woefully unprepared for an oral exam and expected the worst. But Ken "wasn't very tough; he was sympathetic. He was a perfectly lovable gentleman."

Ken remained in demand as an invited speaker at conferences around the world. He went to Harwell, England in 1947; Solvay, Brussels, Belgium in 1947; Mainz, Germany in 1956; Hamilton, Ontario in 1960; Vienna, Austria in 1963; Winnipeg, Manitoba in 1967; and Kyoto, Japan in 1969.

FIGURE 8-6:　Ken and AOC Nier International Conference on Mass Spectrometry Japan 1969

Ken was a member of many scientific societies, including the American Academy of Arts and Sciences (1937) and the National Academy of Sciences (1946). He was also an active member of the American Institute of Physics and the Nobel Prize Committee for Physics. He was also involved in the short-lived Civil Defense Agency of the Commonwealth of Massachusetts.

Ken also served as a consultant to the Navy and Atomic Energy Commission, and many companies, including Bell Telephone, Martin Hubbard, Pneumo Precision, Polaroid, Union Carbide, and the Museum of Science. The children enjoyed playing with flat polarized lenses from Polaroid. Although he was busy, he had more time for family as well.

He was a trustee for Associated Universities and helped Isidor I. Rabi and Norman Ramsey plan and establish the Brookhaven National Laboratory in Upton, New York. This nuclear science research center was created in 1947 by a consortium of nine northeastern universities (Columbia, Cornell, Harvard, Johns Hopkins, M.I.T., Pennsylvania, Princeton, Rochester, and Yale) on a former army camp on Long Island, New York. They realized that Big Physics was now too costly for each to develop their own program. He spent the fall semester at the lab in 1951. The family went along and stayed in the Brookhaven apartments. Joan and Margi were enrolled in the Bellport schools. Margi liked the chance to walk downtown to have lunch at the drug store counter. Ken would return to work on other projects at Brookhaven National Laboratory.

In late 1961, Ken was one of the first members of the Harvard faculty to participate in a new academic exchange program with the Soviet Union. Harvard's sister university was to be the University of Leningrad. Almost concurrent with his arrival in Leningrad, a U.S. spy plane crashed somewhere off Murmansk. This threw a difficult shadow over Ken's relations with his Soviet hosts at first, but the tension relaxed during the two weeks of his stay.

In June 1975, in his last year before his retirement, Ken served on a joint Iran-Harvard planning commission to design Reza Shah Kabir University for Iran. Ken and his Harvard colleagues visited Iran but the project was doomed by the political upheaval and expulsion of the shah.

1946

FIGURE 8-7: Margi, Martin and Joan 1946

FIGURE 8-8: Ken and Margi 1950

FIGURE 8-9: Christmas 1954

Activism

The concern over nuclear risk was clear and Ken worked hard to reduce the risk. One of the goals was to move control from the military to civilian management. This helped lead to the creation of the Atomic Energy Commission. This U.S. federal civilian agency was established by the Atomic Energy Act, and signed into law by President Harry S. Truman on Aug. 1, 1946. Its goal was to better control the development and production of nuclear weapons and to direct the research and development of peaceful uses of nuclear energy. Unfortunately, the commission was soon dominated by military/industrial corporate interests and did little to slow nuclear weapons development. It was abolished in 1975.

FIGURE 8-10:   Physicists against first use of the hydrogen bomb 1950

On February 4, 1950, Ken and ten other prominent nuclear scientists presented the case "as concerned citizens" that the government should pledge to never use the hydrogen bomb first. This received good coverage but did not change policy.

Ken's dislike for the development and testing of nuclear weapons led him to set up a facility to collect and measure radioactive fallout. It is noteworthy that he measured fallout from the first Chinese atomic bomb test as soon as it reached Massachusetts.

He continued work on test bans, arms control, and disarmament. On August 5, 1963, after more than eight years of difficult negotiations, the United States, the United Kingdom, and the Soviet Union signed the Limited Nuclear Test Ban Treaty, reducing the environmental risk but barely slowing testing. Ken continued to work on reducing the threat of nuclear annihilation for the rest of his life.

In the 1950s, vicious attacks on academia were underway by the demagogue Senator Joseph McCarthy and the House Un-American Activities Committee. The witch hunt for "Commies" destroyed thousands of careers. Oppenheimer, who had done so much for American security through his management at Los Alamos, was denied security clearance. His brother Frank, who had been Ken's aide at Trinity, was persecuted, forced to resign from the University of Minnesota and kept out of academia for ten years. The academic vice president at Minnesota sent a letter to Ken requesting information on Frank. The government not only ensured Frank was unable to get a position in the U.S. for a decade, but he was also forbidden to leave the country when offered positions overseas.

It was a time of terror. A 1955 Columbia University study found half of the 2,451 college professors they interviewed feared the witch hunts. McCarthy held a special grudge against Harvard, blaming the university for training a disproportionate number of the foreign service officers at the State Department that he argued were agents of Soviet subversion.

Physicist Dr. Wendell Furry and social science research associate Leon Kamin were among those targeted at Harvard, and their cases dragged on for years. As the chairman and acting treasurer of the Furry support group, Ken generously gave his time and energy to help Dr. Furry. Unanimous support of the department helped raise money for Furry's lawyers. They soon found that the legal defense was going to be much more expensive than expected, so an appeal wider than the department was called for; Ken went to Washington to support Furry. The charges against both Furry and Kamin were dropped in 1956, after two years of torment.

Ken thought new Harvard President Nathan Pusey had done well to see that Furry was retained and promoted. Furry eventually took a turn as the physics department chair. Ken noted that at the time, once a man was a tenured associate professor, all the power for promotion rested with the dean, the president, and the senior fellows.

Ken had worked for J. Robert Oppenheimer, spent time at the home of his Los Alamos aide Frank Oppenheimer in Berkeley (a known radical), and had objected to the witch hunt. While Ken's FBI file grew to almost 50 pages, it never matched Albert Einstein's file of more than 1,400 pages.

FIGURE 8-11:   1960 Horace Mann School Visit

Ken remained an outspoken proponent of civilian control of nuclear power and the abandonment of nuclear testing. His wife Peg became a Quaker and she probably helped shape his work for peace. Despite a lifetime of activism by Ken and many of his colleagues, nuclear tests did not end with the war. By the time the U.S. signed the United Nation's Comprehensive Nuclear Test Ban Treaty in 1996, American physicists and engineers had conducted more than 1,000 tests.

Trinity was never far from Ken's life. In 1965, on the 20th anniversary, Lansing Lamont's book "Day of Trinity" was published. The author interviewed many of the people involved but made several mistakes, or perhaps fell victim to the Rashomon Effect (where everyone involved in an incident sees it in a different way). Ken, as precise as ever, penned several letters, trying to

correct the errors. One of the people Ken wrote to was Oppenheimer. He said he wanted to explain his "Now we are all sons of
bitches" quote, to make sure Oppenheimer understood he was
not trying to be offensive; they had all worked hard to complete
a weapon that would shorten the war, but posterity would judge
it as the creation of an unspeakable weapon. He reiterated this
in a letter to his grandson Greg in 1995. Ken was also saying the
weapon was terrible, and those who contributed to its development must share in any condemnation of it. Those who objected
to the language certainly could not have lived at Trinity for any
length of time.

Oppenheimer wrote back: "When Lamont's book on Trinity
came, I first showed it to Kitty, and a moment later I heard her in
the unseemliest laughter. But despite this, and all else that was
wrong with it, the book was worth something to me because it
recalled your words. We do not have to explain them to anyone."

Ken was a member of the Association of Cambridge Scien-
tists, the Union of Concerned Scientists, and the Federation of
American Scientists. Ken was also active in efforts for justice in
Vietnam, Chile, Cuba, and the search for peace in the Middle
East. He wrote many Letters to the Editor and essays.

Family

Peg was busy with her own work as an educator and activist.
She home-taught high school students who could not come to
school during the polio epidemic, and she taught French and
math at Shady Hills, a private school for grades 4-8.[20] This was a
remarkable school and "the Shady Hill Way" became used not
only by members of the Shady Hill community, but also by out-
siders. Karl T. Compton, the president of MIT during the 1930s,
praised the Shady Hill faculty for emphasizing a problem-solv-
ing approach to "intellectual training." When the school administration asked Peg to teach soccer, she reluctantly stepped
down.

She also did other teaching, including a session at Bates College in Maine, where Ken enjoyed fishing on the Androscoggin River while she taught. She was very active in the PTA and League of Women Voters. She helped found the Cambridge Friends School and served on the Massachusetts Board of Regional Community Colleges (more in chapter 9).

Ken's children married and had children, and he became a loving and loved grandparent. Ken, Peg, and their children spent many summer days in rented cottages overlooking Chilmark Pond, just below Abel's Hill on Martha's Vineyard. They finally decided to buy a lot and build their own house, which was finished just a year before Peg died. The prefabricated 864-square-foot cottage was brought to the site in pieces. It has a deck overlooking the ocean for outside living. With upkeep always a challenge near the sea, Ken's attention to detail and design was evident in the specific instructions he left for his daughters, with replacement materials for the deck carefully stored away. The family would enjoy the cottage for years to come.

Ken suffered a great loss when Peg died in January 1967 after a fall. It had been a loving and supporting partnership for more than 35 years. The Margaret Bainbridge Scholarship Foundation and Memorial Lecture were set up in her honor in Watertown, Massachusetts.

In 1969, Ken married Helen Brinkley King, a friend first met at Princeton forty years prior, when she was acting as a chaperone for her older sister. Helen was a pioneer in her own right, leaving the Old South of Richmond, Virginia to attend the liberal Sarah Lawrence College in New York. Helen had lost her husband, George Broome King, a pilot for PanAm, in an aviation accident in Rio de Janeiro just five years after they married in 1934. In 1969, she was a senior editor at William Morrow Publishing in New York City, representing many best-selling authors.

Retirement

1975–1996

CHAPTER 9

Retirement

At the time, Harvard required faculty to retire at age 70. It had been quite a run. Ken became professor emeritus and would maintain an office at Harvard for the next twenty years. He enjoyed talking physics with his colleagues there, his physics professor son-in-law, and longtime friends. Ken continued to help shape the lives of people who had taken his courses, worked on projects with him, and undertook their dissertations with his guidance. He was well-liked by students, staff, and colleagues, and his work ethic helped encourage all those who worked with him. He got things done while remaining informal, calm, and kind. He continued to take an interest in the physics department and nuclear physics until his death in 1996.

Even in retirement, Ken remained active in support of his beliefs. For example, at a 1985 conference put on by the Union of Concerned Scientists, he protested the Reagan administration's embrace of "Star Wars" defensive weapons, recognizing this would only add another chapter to the Soviet-American arms race, rather than producing more security.

FIGURE 9-2:   Ken and Helen, Menesha Village, Martha's Vineyard

Ken and Helen enjoyed each other's company and were loving and supportive of one another. They split their time between
their home in Weston and the cottage on Martha's Vineyard.
Ken enjoyed his retirement and kept busy with gardening, fishing, puttering about, birdwatching, beach walks, photography,
and mineral collecting. He became an enthusiastic hydroponic

(soil-free) gardener. He also tried to design baffles that would protect his bird feeder from the squirrels.

Throughout his life, Ken frequented art museums, concerts, and musical theater productions; he enjoyed folk music, pop music (the Beatles), and the country-western tunes that had helped keep him awake at work during the war years. One of his western favorites was Cole Porter and Robert Fletcher's "Don't Fence Me In." In retirement, he enrolled in painting classes at the nearby DeCordova Museum and he enjoyed painting on his own.

Ken and Helen traveled to visit family, friends, and former colleagues in the U.S. and abroad. Some of their more notable travels included a 1984 trip with Joan to Los Alamos for a 40th reunion/celebration; and a 1987 trip to Cleveland (Margi's home) to engage with physicist friends at the Michelson Morley Centennial Celebration at Case Western Reserve University. They traveled to Scotland to visit Mary Stewart, an author Helen worked with at William Morrow, and they visited the south of France.

Ken and Helen socialized with friends in town and on Martha's Vineyard, and they were able to enjoy watching Ken's children and grandchildren make their way in the world. Most days, they each worked on the *New York Times* crossword puzzle (using two newspapers). As an editor, Helen was much better at it, and she continued to do some editing work with William Morrow. At her memorial service, it was clear how highly regarded she had been at the firm. Helen was an excellent grandmother and was particularly close to the grandchildren. She was a great listener and encouraged and supported their careers, encouraging everyone to do what they loved. Helen died in 1989, in Middlesex, Massachusetts, and was buried with other family members in historic Hollywood Cemetery, Richmond City, Virginia.

FIGURE 9-3: Ken and grandkids 1974

FIGURE 9-4: Ken's 80th birthday 1984

FIGURE 9-5:   Ken and Helen at the beach 1980

Parents help shape the lives of their children. Peg spent many years with the young children while Ken worked long hours in the war effort. The kids said that throughout his life, when he came home, he was home and present for them. When he took time off, the family played games, went to the beach, and often went fishing. Ken liked ping pong and enjoyed playing matches at the Bartol Foundation, later at Harvard, and at home in the basement.

Peg nurtured Ken and the children, but also set an example of social engagement. She founded the Watertown Citizens for Better Schools and ran for a seat on the school board. She founded the Watertown League of Women Voters, was appointed to the State Board of Directors, and chaired the Education Committee for four productive years. She helped establish schools and a clinic for disabled children. She was well-regarded, and this led to her appointment by the governor to the State Board of Regional Community Colleges to help develop the community college system. She worked hard to get the teacher's colleges certified to offer BA degrees. She spearheaded the drive to fund and build the Friends (Quaker) School in Cambridge.

Even though she was very shy, she forced herself to get out to meet people and build support. She was also very active in town governance and was always ready to help. When conflicts arose, Peg could effectively calm things down. Rather than raising her voice, she lowered it. Like Ken, she made meetings work.

Peg's and Ken's children did well. Daughter Joan earned her A.B. in History and Literature at Harvard/Radcliffe, an M.A. in American History at Columbia University. She taught English and American literature in Bogota, was a research associate at Dartmouth, and after going to law school later in life, a J.D. from Northwestern University. She excelled and, in 1978, became an Assistant United States Attorney for the Northern District of Illinois (NDIL), then Deputy Chief of the Criminal Division (1984), First Assistant U.S. Attorney (1988) and then Deputy United States Attorney (the first woman appointed to the latter two positions in the NDIL). She also served as National and International Security coordinator for the District from 1988–2002. In 2002, she accepted a three-year appointment as United States Department of Justice Attaché to the US Embassy in Mexico City. When she retired from the Department of Justice the Chicago Tribune newspaper headline was, "A fugitive's worst enemy hangs it up." She then spent five years as a consultant for the Procuraduría General de la Républica, Dirección General Extradiciones y Asistencia Jurídica in Mexico City, and continued work on criminal justice and and procedural reform in Latin America until she retired in 2018. She was active in the League of Women Voters in Evanston, Illinois.

Margaret, "Margi," followed in her mother's footsteps. She earned her A.B. in History and Science from Harvard/Radcliffe, was elected to Phi Beta Kappa at Radcliffe. She received a Fulbright Fellowship for a year of graduate study in Paris, in the history and philosophy of mathematics. She taught high school math for a few years, earned an M.A. in mathematics, and, in

1974 entered university administration at Case Western Reserve University as a part-time admissions counselor. Her administrative work gradually increased from part-time to full time as she moved through admissions/academic affairs positions to Associate Dean for Freshmen and then to Dean of Undergraduate Studies, her position for the final 10 years of her 31 year career at CWRU. She retired in 2005. She was a member of the Cleveland Orchestra Chorus for 31 years, including many performances in Cleveland, Europe and Carnegie Hall. She was active in the League of Women Voters in Cleveland Heights, Ohio.

Martin, 'Pidge,' won many model airplane contests as a youth, and wanted to fly real planes. After 2 years at CalTech, he enrolled in the Air Force Officer Candidate School in Texas, was commissioned as a 2nd Lieutenant, and sent to Harlingen AFB for navigator training. After he completed a tour of duty in Bermuda, the Air Force subsidized his undergraduate BS in electrical engineering (Oklahoma State University) and, later, his graduate MS (Air Force Institute of Technology) and MA in Business Administration (Ohio State University). He served in Vietnam, had short-term assignments at many overseas bases, and concluded his Air Force career as a civilian logistician, working on the Air Force technology forecast and procurement at Andrews AFB near Washington, D.C. Sadly, he died of cancer in 1986 at the age of just 52.

Ken died peaceably in 1996. He was still mentally sharp, if perhaps slowed a bit. After reading *the New York Times* one last time and having lunch, he turned out the lights for his nap and was gone. Peg, Ken, Martin, and Martin's son Keith, who died in childhood, are buried in a plot in the small historic cemetery on Abel's Hill, Martha's Vineyard, near their house.

Both of Ken's wives were memorialized with the establishment of scholarships— the Watertown Massachusetts Margaret Bainbridge Scholarship Foundation, and the Helen Brinkley

Bainbridge (Class of 1934) Scholarship Fund for first-year students at Sarah Lawrence College. The grants assist an entering first-year student with an academic and extracurricular record that demonstrates superior overall performance and a genuine concern for the welfare of others.

FIGURE 9-6: Margi and Joan at Trinity 2016

Afterword

During his long career, Ken maintained a high standard of research, scholarship, and willingness to shoulder administrative responsibilities. His contributions were extraordinary. He made an early impact in physics and continued to pioneer in the development of nuclear science for many years. He enjoyed teaching and worked very hard to improve the quality of physics courses for high school, undergraduate and graduate students, and post doctoral students.

Ken was well-liked and his work ethic inspired all who worked with him. He was described by those who knew him as quiet and dedicated to his science. "A very fine individual—very thoughtful, very conscientious, very hard-working, almost meticulous," said Norman F. Ramsey, Higgins Professor of Physics Emeritus.

Ken was cognizant of the dangers his discoveries shaped, and he was courageous enough to act. After World War II, he actively opposed nuclear testing and the escalating arms race, and was one of twelve scientists who lobbied President Harry S. Truman to promise that the United States would not be the first country to use a hydrogen bomb. He continued his work to limit the risk of nuclear weapons into his eighties.

Ken took stands against prejudice in church, property ownership, and education. He was also a staunch defender of academic freedom. As chair of Harvard's Physics Department in the 1950s, he opposed the activities of Senator Joseph McCarthy and the House Un-American Activities Committee.

Ken set an excellent example for others to follow. Be kind, respect your students and colleagues, work hard, listen well, and find the humor in life's inevitable challenges.

Notes

1 In a recent Niche survey, it was ranked as third best K-12 private school in the country, out of 2,525.
2 R R Dourmashkin MD. 1997. What caused the 1918-30 epidemic of *encephalitis lethargica*? Journal of the Royal Society of Medicine. 90:515-520.
3 Academic Entreprenuership and Engineering Education:Dugald G. Jackson and the MIT_GE Cooperative Engineering Course 1907-1932. Technology and Culture 29(3):536-567.
4 TBΠ honors students of exemplary character and distinguished scholarship as engineering students and alumni, based on their academic performance, recommendations from faculty, and contributions to engineering and the society.
5 Compton won the Nobel prize in physics 1927.
6 Smyth wrote "Atomic Energy for Military Purposes" in 1945, Princeton University Press, and played a crucial role in the adoption of the Nuclear Non-Proliferation Treaty in 1970.
7 KT Bainbridge.1933. The equivalence of Mass and Energy. *Physical Review.* 44:123.
8 Cockroft and Walton would win the Nobel Prize for this work in 1951.
9 Based on the English practice where the student would meet for an hour or so with a faculty member every week and be guided in research and education.
10 She was a prize-winning potter, originally from Taos Pueblo but had married into San Ildefonso.
11 Popovi Da was also an accomplished potter, the son of the internationally acclaimed potter, Maria Montoya Martinez, "Po-Ve-Ka."
12 Tilano had crossed the Atlantic in his youth and seen the great cities— London, Paris, Berlin, Rome, and more as a member of a Pueblo dance group. He especially liked Paris.
13 Safing devices can de-arm an explosive once it is activated.
14 The original unit used to express the decay rate of a sample of radioactive material.
15 Hanford, Washington, was the site was the site of the B Reactor, the first full-scale plutonium production reactor in the world.

16 A detailed estimate was not done until 2020. Cahoon et al. 2020. Projected
Cancer Risks to Residents of New Mexico from Exposure to Trinity
Radioactive Fallout. Health Physics, 119(4), 478–493.

17 Oppenheimer had suffered a severe case of trench dysentery in a visit to
Germany as a young man. He returned to the U.S. on a stretcher. His low
weight may have been related to the lifelong consequences of structural gut
damage, now called environmental enteric dysfunction.

18 Compounds with the same formula but a different arrangement of atoms in
the molecule.

19 A full professor is entitled to a paid year off every 6 or 7 years in many
universities. This is to recharge, catch up on research and writing and to
explore new topics.

20 400 students at the time, including Ken's children Martin and Margi.

Image Credits

The challenge of using historical photos is finding out who took them, when, who might have copyright, and where the best quality print can be found. Think about your own box (or file) of unlabeled photos and multiply it by a factor of 100. I spent weeks simply working on image origin and permissions. Copyright permissions were placed at the back of the book, rather than on or under the photo in the text, to improve design.

The web has made it easier to find images, but these are often used without any note of where they came from. Some are used in a chain of copies — and like the children's game "telephone," lose details with each reuse. A few were easy, most were not. Ken's family graciously searched through their boxes of photos and shared them with me.

Many archivists, librarians and staff worked diligently to help me, working above and beyond what might have been expected within their Covid19 control restrictions. Any misattribution that may occur will be corrected in future editions—please send details to me at sustainabilityleader@gmail.com.

David A. Bainbridge, San Diego

Ch.	#	Image Credits/Copyrights
1	1	Robert W. Bainbridge
1	2	KTB family
1	3	KTB family
1	4	KTB family
1	5	db, Ephemeral New York, KTB family
1	6	Horace Mann School
1	7	Courtesy Camp Moosilauke
1	8	Courtesy of Teacher's College, Columbia University/Horace Mann School
1	9	Courtesy of Teacher's College, Columbia University
1	10	Horace Mann School
1	11	postcards
1	12	Horace Mann School
2	1	Courtesy MIT
2	2	Courtesy MIT
2	3	miSci, Museum of Innovation and Science
2	4	Courtesy General Electric
2	5	Courtesy General Electric
2	6	Courtesy MIT
2	7	Courtesy MIT
3	1	Courtesy of Princeton University Library
3	2	By permission Patience Hutty Kotorman
3	3	Henry DeWolf Smyth Papers, American Philosophical Society
3	4	Courtesy Princeton University
3	5	Courtesy of and copyright the Cavendish Laboratory, Cambridge University
3	6	Courtesy and copyright BAE Systems
3	7	db
4	1	Friends Historical Library, Swarthmore College
4	2	KTB family

Ch.	#	Image Credits/Copyrights
4	3	KTB family
4	4	Courtesy Harvard University
4	5	Guggenheim Fndt Report 1933-34
4	6	Courtesy of and copyright the Cavendish Laboratory, Cambridge University
4	7	Courtesy of and copyright the Cavendish Laboratory, Cambridge University
4	8	Courtesy of and copyright the Cavendish Laboratory, Cambridge University
4	9	Courtesy UK Atomic Energy Authority
4	10	Courtesy of and copyright the Cavendish Laboratory, Cambridge University
4	11	db Google Earth
5	1	Courtesy Physics Department, Harvard University
5	2	Niels Bohr Library, American Institute of Physics Emilio Segrè Visual Archives, Bainbridge Collection
5	3	Kenneth T. Bainbridge
5	4	Niles Bohr Library, American Institute of Physics Emilio Segrè Visual Archives, Physics Today Collection
5	5	US Patent Office
5	6	HUGFP 152 Box 43, Folder: Cyclotron Photos, ca. 1930 [Folder 2]. Harvard University Archives.
5	7	Courtesy Harvard University
5	8	16064 Box 4. Harvard University Archives.
6	1	Courtesy MIT Lincoln Lab
6	2	MIT Radiation Lab, Courtesy MIT Museum
6	3	db
6	4	courtesy Stig Hertze Telia
6	5	db
6	6	MIT Radiation Laboratory. Courtesy MIT Museum

Ch.	#	Image Credits/Copyrights
6	7	Gift of Kenneth T. Bainbridge. Courtesy MIT Museum
6	8	MIT Radiation Laboratory Collection. Courtesy MIT Museum
6	9	db
6	10	Courtesy Stig Hertze Telia
6	11	db
6	12	db
6	13	Australian War Memorial
6	14	KTB family
7	1	National Building Museum
7	2	National Building Museum, DOE
7	3	LANL
7	4	LANL
7	5	Zia Project 1942 view to west LANL
7	6	KTB family
7	7	KTB family
7	8	Henry Shadel, Photo courtesy of Los Alamos National Laboratory, Bradbury Science Museum
7	9	Sketch adapted from Los Alamos History Museum photo
7	10	New Mexico History Museum
7	11	db
7	12	db
7	13	Source: Department of Energy, Manhattan Project
7	14	LANL
7	15	LANL
7	16	LANL
7	17	db
7	18	LANL
7	19	db
7	20	LANL

Ch.	#	Image Credits/Copyrights
7	21	LANL
7	22	LANL
7	23	LANL
7	24	Berlyn Brixner, Julian Mack LANL
7	25	LANL
7	26	Source: Center for Disease Control
7	27	LANL
8	1	LANL TR 69C
8	2	Harvard University archives
8	3	db
8	4	KTB family
8	5	HUP Bainbridge, Kenneth T. (2). Harvard University Archives
8	6	By permission Ardis Nier
8	7	KTB family
8	8	Norton Hintz by permission Mary Abbe Hintz
8	9	KTB family
8	10	Courtesy Associated Press Wire Photo
8	11	HUGFP 152 Box 3, Folder: Photographs ca. 1960s. Harvard University Archives
9	1	KTB family
9	2	KTB family
9	3	KTB family
9	4	KTB family
9	5	KTB family
9	6	KTB family
14	1	Comprehensive Nuclear-Test-Ban Treaty Organization
14	2	db using NukeMap 2.7

Sources

I relied on Ken's own words, articles, and writing whenever possible. He did several interviews, and oral histories were also helpful. His family graciously provided insight, photos, and stories. His daughters Joan and Margi were very helpful and provided information and editorial support. Grandson Greg Robinson shared a letter Ken wrote in 1995 about his feelings on the bomb. Brief mentions of Ken were made in many other oral histories of the scientists and staff at Los Alamos and the Radiation Lab. The American Institute of Physics has done an excellent job of collecting these stories.

Bainbridge, K. T. 1940. The Harvard Cyclotron. *Harvard Alumni Bulletin*, 17 May 1010–1015.

Bainbridge, K. T. 1976 [1946]. *Trinity*. Los Alamos National Laboratory, Los Alamos, NM. LA-6300-H.

Bainbridge, K. T. and J. Safford. 1964. The Reminiscences of Kenneth T. Bainbridge, oral history interview conducted by his daughter Joan Safford, Columbia University Oral History Research Office.

Bainbridge, K. T. 1975. Prelude to Trinity. *The Bulletin of Atomic Scientists.* 31(April):42–46.

Bainbridge, K. T. 1975. A Foul and Awesome Display. *The Bulletin of Atomic Scientists.* 31(May):40–46.

Bainbridge, K. T. 1977. Interview of Kenneth Bainbridge by Katherine Sopka on March 16. Niels Bohr Library & Archives, American Institute of Physics, College Park, MD. www.aip.org/history-programs/niels-bohr-library/oral-histories/31507-1

Bainbridge, K. T. 1985. D. W. Taylor interview with Kenneth Tompkins Bainbridge. Naval Ship Research and Development Center. Bethesda. DTNSRDC-85/CT02.

Bainbridge, K. T. 1991. Electrical Engineer. Interview conducted by John Bryant, IEEE History Center, 10 June 1991. Interview # 73 for the IEEE History Center, The Institute of Electrical and Electronics Engineers, Inc. Rutgers.

Freeman, K. 1996. Kenneth Bainbridge, 91, Chief of First Test of Atomic Bomb. *The New York Times.* Jul 18.

Pound, R. V. 1997. Kenneth Tompkins Bainbridge. *Physics Today.* 50: 80–82.

Pound, R. V. and N. F. Ramsey. 1999. Kenneth Tompkins Bainbridge, July 27, 1904-July 14, 1996. *Biographical Memoirs, Volume 76.* National Academy Press.

Sopka, K. R. 1978. Physics at Harvard During the Past Half-Century: A Brief Departmental History. Harvard University.

Wilson, R. nd. A Brief History of the Harvard University Cyclotrons. Physics Department, Harvard. (retrieved 2021)

Wilson, R. nd. Kenneth (Ken) Tompkins Bainbridge. Biographical Memoir. wilsonweb.physics.harvard.edu (retrieved 2021)

Books and reports of interest related to KTB
Bird, K. and M. J. Sherwin 2006. *American Prometheus: The Triumph and Tragedy of J. Robert Oppenheimer.* Vintage. (There are more than ten books about him, and he is seen in very different ways).

Brown, L. 1999. *Technical and Military Imperatives: A Radar History of World War II.* Carnegie Institution of Washington. Institute of Physics Publishing Bristol and Philadelphia.

Gaulkin, T. 2020. In Their Own Words: Trinity at 75. *Bulletin of Atomic Scientists.* July. https://thebulletin.org/2020/07/in-their-own-words-trinity-at-75/

Goldberg, S. 1987. Women at Los Alamos. December 2, Boston, Manhattan Project session eleven. Smithsonian Video History 9531.

Hawkins, D., E. C. Truslow and R. C. Smith. 1961 [1946/1947] *Project Y: The Los Alamos Project from Inception to December 1946.* Los Alamos Scientific Laboratory of the University of California. US AEC. W-6405-ENG 36.

Kunetka, J. 2015. *The General and the Genius.* Regnery History.

Merlan, T. 2001. *Life at Trinity Base Camp.* Human Systems Research, Inc. for White Sands Missile Range.

Norris, R. S. 2002. *Racing for the Bomb: The True Story of General Leslie R. Groves.* Steerforth Press. (Like Oppie, General Groves is portrayed in very different ways, including his own autobiography).

Rhodes, R. 2012 [1986]. *The Making of the Atomic Bomb.* Simon and Schuster.

Summary Reports Group of the Columbia University Division of War Research. 1946. Bibliography of Division 14 and Radiation Laboratory Reports. National Defense Research Committee. Washington DC. Contract OEMsr-1131. Columbia University Press.

Acknowledgments

My special thanks to the members of Ken's family for their support, contributions to editing, and images. His daughters Joan Safford and Margaret Robinson were particularly helpful, but the grandchildren contributed technical support and comments as well.

My editors and reviewers helped me improve the flow, accuracy, and impact of the writing. Special thanks to Sutton Mason, Laurie Lippitt, Al Hyatt, Robert W. Bainbridge, and others who read a chapter or two.

Many people helped with research despite Covid restrictions. Key information came from staff and archivists at Horace Mann School, Teacher's College of Columbia University, Camp Moosilauke, the Cavendish Lab at Cambridge, England; MIT University, Niels Bohr Library, Harvard University Physics Department, Library and Archives; Princeton University Library, The Atomic Heritage Foundation, American Institute of Physics (an excellent series of oral interviews), the American Philosophical Society, Los Alamos National Labs, Bradbury Museum, *the New York Times*, and many others who helped capture Ken's life and work.

Images were sourced from many places, as you can see in the image credits. The Neils Bohr Library made the Emilio Segré Images of Physics available — a great project. The Los Alamos National Lab and Bradbury Museum also have excellent collections and provided assistance, as did the Los Alamos History Museum. Horace Mann School and Teacher's College at Columbia University went above and beyond in sleuthing their files for images. Harvard, MIT, Princeton, the Cambridge Digital Library, General Electric, BAE Systems, and many others helped me find images and identify copyright holders. Thank you all!

Books and Papers

Books

Bainbridge, KT and AO Nier. 1950. Relative isotopic abundances of the elements. *Report of the Nuclear Science Series.* #9:1–59.

Bainbridge, KT and PJ van Heerden. 1950. *Laboratory Manual for Experiments in Nuclear Physics and X-Rays.* 96 pages.

Bainbridge, KT. 1948. Isotopic weights of the fundamental isotopes. *Preliminary Report of the Nuclear Science Series.* #1:1–20.

Bainbridge, KT. 1976 [1946]. *Trinity* (NTIS Accession no. DE82 010104)

Book Chapters and Proceedings

Bainbridge, KT et al. 1997. Jabez Curry Street 1906–1989. *National Academy Press Biographical Memoirs.* 71:346–355.

Kerr DP and KT Bainbridge. 1970. Mass measurements of Te^{130}, Xe^{130}, Te^{128}, Xe^{128} and Te^{126} and the current status of the lock in amplifier methods. pp. 490–494. In *Proceedings of the 1969 Int'l Conference on Mass Spectroscopy*, Kyoto.

Bainbridge, KT and J.W. Dewdney. 1967. Use of a lock in amplifier for mass doublet measurements by the coincidence method. pp. 758–775. In *Proceedings of the Third Int'l Conference on Nucleic Masses.*

Bainbridge KT. 1963. A direct determination of the ^{3}H-^{3}E mass difference. In WH Johnson Jr. ed. In *Proceedings International Conference on Nucleic Masses*. Vienna, Austria. Springer-Verlag.

Moreland, PE Jr. and KT Bainbridge. 1960. The mass spectrometer at Harvard University. pp. 460–473 In *International Conference on Nucleic Masses*. University of Toronto Press.

Bainbridge, KT. 1959. The present status of the determination of nuclear masses. pp. 5–19 In *Proceedings of the Conference on Nuclear Masses and Their Determination*. Mainz, Germany. Pergamon Press.

Collins TL and KT Bainbridge. 1957. A Large Mass Spectrograph. pp. 213–217. In *Proceedings of the Conference on Nuclear Masses and Their Determination*. Max Planck Institute. Mainz, Germany. Pergamon Press.

Bainbridge KT. 1953. Charged particle dynamics and optics, relative isotopic abundance of the elements atomic masses. pp. 559–766. In E Segre, ed. *Experimental Nuclear Physics*. John Wiley and Sons.

Bainbridge KT. 1947. Some results of mass spectrum analysis. pp. 55–96. In *Proceedings Solvay Conference in Chemistry*. Belgium.

Papers: 1975

Bainbridge, KT. A foul and awesome display. *Bulletin of the Atomic Scientists*. 31(5): 40–46.

Bainbridge, KT. Prelude to Trinity. *Bulletin of the Atomic Scientists*. 31(4): 42–46.

Papers: 1971

Kerr, D and KT Bainbridge. The ^{14}ND–^{15}NH Mass Difference. *CanJPhysics* 49(14):1950–1951.

Kerr, D and KT Bainbridge. The ^{235}U–^{207}Pb and ^{238}U–^{206}Pb Mass Differences. *CanJPhysics* 49(6):756–760.

Papers: 1969

Olin A and KT Bainbridge. Influence of superconductivity on the half-life of niobium-^{90m}. *Physical Review.* 179: 450–452.

Papers: 1966

Malliaris AC, and KT Bainbridge. Alteration of the decay constant of Te^{125m} by chemical means. *Physical Review.* 149:958–964.

Papers: 1965

Dewdney JW and KT Bainbridge. Masses of the stable chlorine isotopes *Physical Review.* 138: B540-B544.

Papers: 1953

Kraushaar JJ, ED Wilson KT Bainbridge. Comparison of the values of the disintegration constant of Be^7 in Be, BeO, and BeF$_2$. *Physical Review.* 90:610–614.

Bainbridge KT, M. Goldhaber and E Wilson. Influence of the chemical state on the lifetime of a nuclear isomer, Tc^{99m} *Physical Review.* 90:430–439.

Papers: 1951

Bainbridge KT, M Goldhaber and E Wilson. Influence of the chemical state on the lifetime of an isomer. *Physical Review.* 84:1260–1261.

Bainbridge KT. The isotopic weight of helium. *Physical Review.* 81:146–147.

Bartlett AA and KT Bainbridge. A high resolution two-directional focusing beta-ray spectrometer. *Review of Scientific Instruments.* 22:517–523.

Purcell, EM and KT Bainbridge. The effect of the Hartree Potential in nuclear transition. *Physical Review.* 83:1

Papers: 1950
Bainbridge, KT and AO Nier. Relative Isotopic Abundances of the Elements, *Preliminary Report No. 9, Nuclear Science Series*, National Academy of Science - National Research Council, Wash. DC.

Papers: 1949
Bainbridge KT. Fringing field corrections for magnetic sector lenses and prims. *Physical Review.* 75. 2164.

Papers: 1947
Bainbridge KT. On the paucity of positive particles from P^{32}. Progress Report. N5-ori-76, Task IV. Mentioned in *Nature* 160:492.

Papers: 1942
Bainbridge, KT. Interim Report of the Problems and Activities of Group G. Jan. 12.

Papers: 1941
Bainbridge KT. RL-30 Considerations Affecting Choice of Wavelength, Sept. 24, 1941. RL-120.

Sherr R, KT Bainbridge and HH Anderson. Transmutation of mercury by fast neutrons. *Physical Review.* 60:473–479.

Papers: 1940
Bainbridge KT. The Harvard Cyclotron. *Harvard Alumni Bulletin*. May 17.

Papers: 1939
Bainbridge KT and R Sherr. Geissler tube protection of oil vapor pumps. *Review of Scientific Instruments*. 10:316.

Papers: 1938
Baxter GP, Hönigschmid O, Lebeau P, Aston FW, Bainbridge KT, Jordan EB, Hale AH, Scott AF, Hurley FH, Wittmann G, Witter F, Menn W, Nier AOC, Moles E, Toral T, et al. *Atomgewichte. Zeitschrift FüR Analytische Chemie.* 112:342–345.

Papers: 1937
Bainbridge, KT and EB Jordan. Minutes of the Atlantic City Meeting, December 28–30, 1936. *Physical Review* 51:373.

Papers: 1936
Jordan EB and KT Bainbridge. A mass-spectrographic determination of the mass difference $N^{14}+H^1-N^{15}$ and the nitrogen disintegration reactions. *Physical Review.* 50: 98.

Bainbridge KT, and EB Jordan. Mass spectrum analysis 1. the mass spectrograph. 2. the existence of isobars of adjacent elements. *Physical Review.* 50: 282–296.

Bainbridge KT. Comparison of the masses of H^2 and helium. *Physical Review.* 44:57.

Bainbridge KT. The masses of the lithium isotopes. *Physical Review.* 44: 56–57.

Bainbridge KT. The equivalence of mass and energy. *Physical Review*. 44:123.

Bainbridge KT. The masses of Ne^{20} and B^{11}. the mass of Ne^{22} and the disintegration of F^{19} *Physical Review*. 43:424–427.

Bainbridge KT. The mass of Be^9 and the atomic weight of beryllium. *Physical Review*. 43:367–368.

Bainbridge KT. Comparison of the masses of He and H^1 on a mass-spectrograph. *Physical Review*. 43:103–105.

Bainbridge KT. The masses of atoms and the structure of atomic nuclei. *Journal of the Franklin Institute*. 215:509–534.

Papers: 1932

Bainbridge KT. The isotopic weight of H^2. *Physical Review*. 42:1–10.

Bainbridge KT. The isotopic constitution of zinc. *Physical Review*. 39:847–848.

Bainbridge KT. The constitution of tellurium. *Physical Review*. 39:1021.

Papers: 1931

Bainbridge KT. The blackening of photographic plates by positive ions of the alkali metals. *Journal of the Franklin Institute*. 212:489–506.

Bainbridge KT. The isotopes of lithium, sodium, and potassium. *Journal of the Franklin Institute*. 212:317–339.

Papers: 1930

Bainbridge KT. Simple isotopic constitution of caesium. *Physical Review*. 36:1668.

Papers: 1929

Bainbridge KT. A search for element 87 by analysis of positive rays. *Physical Review.* 34:752–762.

Bainbridge KT. *A search for element 87*. Doctoral Dissertation. Princeton University. 19p.

Papers: 1926

Bainbridge, KT. Liquid conductor pump: theory and development for commercial applications. MIT.

Patents

1953. 2658147 Tunable velocity modulation device (filed 1946)

1953. 2653238 Dual frequency antenna (filed 1945)

1953. 2658147 Tunable velocity modulation device (filed 1946) lost on appeal

1951. 2577502 Directional radar system (filed 1945)

1940. 2206713 Photoelectric apparatus (filed 1929)

1933. 1901578 Method of preparing Photo electric tubes (filed 1928)

1933. 1901577 Photo electric tube (filed 1928)

1930. 1747044 Circuit controlling apparatus (filed 1926)

1928. 1660407 Liquid conductor pump (filed 1926)

In 1939 a KTB patent application was denied in a conflict with a British application, GE records were found to be insufficient, not that Ken had not done the work earlier.

Other books by the author

Tenacity: Remarkable People of the Fur War (2021)

Fur War: The Political, Economic, Cultural and Ecological Impacts of the Western Fur Trade 1765–1840 (2020)

Gardening with Less Water (2015); Silver Nautilus Award

The Raven Chronicles (2012); poetry

Passive Solar Architecture (2011); Boston Bookbuilders Award, best professional reference

A Guide for Desert and Dryland Restoration (2007)

The Straw Bale House (1994); Bestseller

Sustainable Agriculture for California: A Guide to Information (1991)

The Second Passive Solar Catalog (1980); Honoree, San Francisco Book Festival

Village Homes' Solar House Designs (1979)

Quantitative Land Capability Analysis (1979)

The First Passive Solar Catalog (1979)

Waterglass (1979); poetry

100 Seconds to Midnight

The Doomsday Clock was created by Atomic Scientists to warn the public about how close we are to destroying our world with dangerous technologies of our own making. The day gets shorter and shorter as we approach catastrophe. https://thebulletin.org/doomsday-clock/

FIGURE 14-1: French Licorn 914 Kiloton Test in the Pacific 1970

Despite the best efforts of Ken and many of his colleagues, nuclear tests did not end with the war. By the time the U.S. signed the United Nations Comprehensive Nuclear Test Ban Treaty in 1996, American physicists and engineers had conducted more than 1,000 tests. They set them off on land, underground, on islands, in and on the ocean, and in space. In 1952, a 10-megaton H-bomb test vaporized the island of Elugelab.

A well-funded army of U.S. weapons scientists blew up a nuclear weapon every chance they got, at one point averaging one detonation a week. The Cold War led to rapid buildups of nuclear weapons, peaking at about 70,000. The world's combined inventory of nuclear warheads today has dropped to 13,000. More than 9,000 are in military stockpiles (the rest are in various stages of being disassembled). About 1,900 U.S., Russian, British and French warheads are on high alert, ready for use on short notice. Nine countries have nuclear weapons.

The largest atomic bomb ever detonated was set off by Russia in 1961. This was estimated at 57 megatons (about 3,000 times larger than the Trinity explosion in 1945) even with dampers installed to limit the size of the blast. Undamped, it might have been 100 megatons.

There have been deadly accidents, alerts, and close calls, but so far, no use of atomic bombs in conflicts or terrorist acts. This threat is still one of the bigger risks to humankind. Much more needs to be done to reduce stockpiles and make nuclear terrorism less likely.

Nuclear Risk

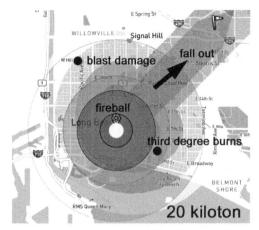

35,000 killed　63,000 injured

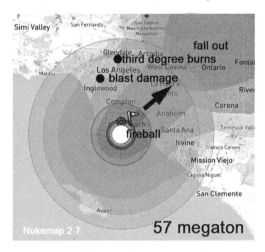

1 million killed　3 million injured

FIGURE 14-2:　Atomic damage and fatalities projection for Long Beach ground zero atomic blasts done using NukeMap 2.7

Made in the USA
Las Vegas, NV
11 March 2022

45485716R00105